The Bedside Book of
Irish Fables and L

Maureen

MERCIER PRESS

Mercier Press
PO Box 5, 5 French Church Street, Cork
24 Lower Abbey Street, Dublin 1

ISBN 1 85635 063 0

This edition 1993

For My Mother

Acknowledgement
*I wish to acknowledge the help and co-operation of the librarian
and staff of the University College Library, Cork.*

Printed in Ireland by Colour Books Ltd.

CONTENTS

THE BOYHOOD OF CUCHULAINN

Cuchulainn's family background was both complicated and mysterious. When Fergus, king of Ulster, asked the widow Ness to marry him she made one condition.

'I will be your wife,' she said, 'if you let my son Conchobor be king for just one year in your place, so that his children will be called the sons of kings.'

Conchobor's father, Fachtna, had been the king of Ulster before Fergus. In reality he had been a druid, named Cathba, and there were powers at work at which not even Fergus could guess. Ness had a gentle manner which hid iron resolution: something else her husband-to-be did not realise. He only knew that he wanted her and that Conchobor was a fatherless youth. It did not seem particularly dangerous to indulge her whim.

'That is all you want,' he asked, smiling, 'for your marriage portion?'

'That is all I want,' Ness said.

Fergus consulted the men of Ulster.

'Call him king if you like,' they said, 'but it will be in name only. You are our king.' So Fergus and Ness were married and Conchobor was crowned.

Ness used the year well. She schemed and she plotted and she gave presents to the chiefs of Ulster. At the same time she encouraged Conchobor in his warrior skills and although he was young he was brave in battle and, with Ness's help, wise beyond his years. The men of Ulster took to him and when Fergus asked for the kingship back at the end of the year they told him they preferred Conchobor.

'Let him stay king,' they said, 'and you keep your wife.'

There was nothing Fergus could do without the support

of his chiefs and so he retired with as much good grace as was possible and Conchobor's reign continued.

Conchobor lived in great splendour. His palace at Emain Macha had three huge buildings: the Royal Branch, where visiting kings stayed; the Red Branch, where the heads and arms of conquered enemies were kept; and the Speckled House, where warriors were obliged to lodge their weapons before going into a banquet, to avoid drunken quarrels turning into wholesale slaughter. This house, aptly named, gleamed gold and silver in the speckled light reflected from shields, armour and spears. The palace contained one hundred and fifty rooms in total, made of red oak and decorated with copper but Conchobor's own room was bordered in bronze and silver and jewelled golden emblems. It was large enough for thirty warriors to drink in it together and, to facilitate this, a large vat full of good drink always stood on the floor. Above the king's chair hung his silver wand with three golden apples. When he shook it silence reigned throughout the palace. He was a man who liked the good life and who fed on power. To continue like this he needed loyal soldiers and champion warriors.

When Conchobor's sister, Dechtire, married Sualtim, son of Roig, the king ordered a huge feast and the men and girls of Ulster flocked to the great banqueting hall. Dechtire was very thirsty and she drank deeply from a cup of wine. As she did so a mayfly flew into the wine and Dechtire swallowed it by accident.

'I feel very sleepy,' she said after a while. She got up and beckoned her fifty maidens and went into her own bright room and fell into a deep sleep. In a dream Lugh of the Long Hand, a god of magic, appeared to Dechtire.

'I was the mayfly in the cup,' he said, 'and now you and your women must come with me.'

'How can this be?' Dechtire asked.

'I will turn you all into a flock of birds,' Lugh said. Dechtire realised too late that it was not a dream.

They flew southwards to Brugh na Boinne and lived

there with the *Sidhe*, the fairy people, whose music could sometimes be heard faintly on the wind. No one at Emain knew where they were, or how they had been spirited away but, a year later, at yet another royal feast, a huge flock of birds flew over the palace and landed on the lawn and proceeded to eat every blade of grass in sight. The men of Ulster were annoyed. Conchobor ordered chariots to be yoked to follow the birds and capture them but the birds led them on an endless chase. Fergus, who had by now accepted Conchobor as king and friend, went with him and so did Celthair, Laegaire, Bricriu of the Bitter Tongue and many others.

They went south, the whole length of the country, with the flock always a little ahead of them and the men of Ulster had to admit that the flight of birds was the most beautiful sight they had ever seen. There were nine groups, linked together in twos by a silver chain and, at the head of each group, were two birds of different colours and they were linked by a golden chain. Three others flew by themselves and the men of Ulster followed them across hill and forest until night fell and they could no longer see them.

'We will have to find somewhere to sleep for the night,' Conchobor said.

Fergus looked around and found nearby a small, ill-made house with a man and a woman in it. The house was poor and the occupants were shabbily dressed but they made Fergus welcome.

'Bring your friends in,' they said, 'and they can share what we have.'

So Fergus went back to his companions and told them what he had found.

'There's no point in going to a place like that,' Bricriu said. 'There won't be any food, or coverings for us, or even the space to lie down.' Bricriu liked his comforts.

'Then you'd better go and tell them so yourself,' Fergus said, 'I've done all I can.'

Bricriu sighed and got to his feet and went off in the

7

direction that Fergus pointed out but instead of a poor cottage he found a large new, well-lighted house with a tall handsome man in armour standing at the door.

'Come in Bricriu,' the man said, 'and don't look so surprised.'

There was a beautiful young woman beside him. She also held out her hand.

'You are more than welcome,' she said to Bricriu.

'I don't understand why you should welcome a stranger,' Bricriu said.

'It is on account of her that I welcome you,' the young man said, indicating the girl. 'Haven't you missed anyone at Emain, recently?'

'We have indeed,' Bricriu said. 'Fifty young maidens for the length of a year.'

'And would you know them again?' the young man asked.

'I'm not sure,' Bricriu said. 'A year is a long time. They might have changed.'

'Then have a close look,' the young man said, 'because they are here in my house and this girl beside me is Dechtire. They went to Emain Macha as a flock of birds to bring you here.'

Dechtire gave Bricriu a lovely purple cloak with golden fringes and he went back to show it to his companions. But on the way it occurred to him that Conchobor might reward him for finding his sister and her maidens and that the less he said the better.

'Well?' Conchobor said, 'What news?'

'I found a brightly-lit house,' Bricriu said, 'and a beautiful young queen with curly hair. She was very regal and kind. The man of the house was courteous too. He will make us welcome.'

'Good', Conchobor said. 'Then we will spend the night there.'

'We should be very comfortable,' Bricriu said. As an afterthought he added, 'there were plenty of handsome young women to serve us too.'.

As soon as they arrived at the house they were given every kind of food and drink. When they had eaten and drunk their fill Conchobor asked the young man where the mistress of the house was, so that they could thank her.

'You cannot see her tonight,' the young man said. 'She is in the pains of childbirth'.

'Then give her our good wishes,' Conchobor said.

They were all given comfortable rooms and they slept well. In the morning Conchobor was the first up. As he was dressing he heard the cry of a new-born baby. The crying led him to an upper room and there he found Dechtire and her maidens.

'Welcome brother,' she said, and held out her hand.

'So you are the kind queen who has given us shelter,' he said. 'How can it be?'

It took some time for Dechtire to tell him all that had happened to her: the cup of wine and the mayfly and Lugh of the Long Hand and how she and her maidens had been turned into a flock of birds.

'And I sent them back to Emain Macha to tell you where I was so that I might go home to you,' she said, finally.

'And you have given us a gift of a child,' he said, 'a very special child.'

By this time the men of Ulster had crowded into the room and were marvelling at the sight of Dechtire and the fifty missing girls.

'We will ask our sister, Finchoem, to bring up the child,' Conchobor was saying.

'No,' said Sencha, the chief poet, who was just in time to hear this remark. 'I am the one to bring up this child. I am skilled and good at argument; I am the one who is asked to judge royal quarrels and no one but the king has the right to dispute my claim to this special child.'

'Give the child to me,' Blai said. 'I will see to his every need. I am the one who organises and victuals the soldiers of Conchobor; I settle their disagreements and keep their honour safe and avenge their wrongs.'

'You think too much of yourself,' Fergus said, 'I am the king's messenger and I have honour and riches above you all. I am an experienced soldier and a protector of the weak.'

'Be quiet, everyone,' Amergin said, 'I can bring the child up like a king. I am known for my honour and bravery and my courage and wisdom. And I am a poet and have gentleness in me. Give him to me, Conchobor.'

'Let Finchoem keep the child for the moment,' Sencha said, silencing the voices around him, 'and we will ask Morann, the judge at Emain Macha to decide.'

'Don't forget that I was the one to find them,' Bricriu said to Conchobor as they left the chamber.

The next day they set out for Conchobor's palace, the soldiers, the maidens, Dechtire and the baby. They got a great welcome on the lawns at Emain Macha and Dechtire brought the child inside to be admired.

'He is Conchobor's next of kin,' Morann the judge said. 'Let Conchobor name him and Sencha teach him words and Fergus hold him on his knee. Amergin can be his tutor and this child will be ours.' The men of Ulster cheered and Morann went on, 'He will be celebrated for all time by kings and warriors and wise men; he will be well loved and he will fight all our causes; he will defend all our fords and avenge our wrongs.'

Sualtim, Dechtire's husband, undertook to care for the child and so the baby was brought up by his mother, until he came to an age of reason. He lived with Dechtire and Sualtim at Muirthemne and he was known as Setanta, son of Sualtim.

When he was about seven he asked Dechtire if he might go and play with the children at the court. 'They spend all their time at games and hurling,' he said, 'and I have heard people talking about what happens at the palace.'

'You are too young,' she said. 'Wait until you are older and then I'll get someone to look after you on the way.'

'I can't wait for that,' said Setanta, already showing the signs of the man he was to become. 'Tell me the way and I'll go myself.'

'It is too far,' Dechtire said, 'it is beyond Slieve Fuad.'

'East or west?' he asked.

'West,' his mother said and the little boy went to collect his hurling stick.

He travelled with a dart, a spear, a silver ball and the hurling stick. Like all children, he amused himself by hitting the ball with the stick and then sending the dart after it and running to pick them up before they fell. He hardly noticed the length of the road and it seemed to be no time at all before he came to the lawns at Emain Macha.

For a while he stood watching the sons of kings hurling and learning the use of arms. After a while he went in after the ball himself and drove it along and scored a goal before anyone could stop him.

'Who does this stranger think he is?' Follaman, Conchobor's son shouted.

'How dare he join our game.'

The others gathered round and then made a concerted attack on the little boy. They went for him with their hurling sticks and their darts but he wriggled away from them and then turned and attacked them in return. Fergus, who had just come out of the palace, saw what was happening and how well the child defended himself. He went over and brought him into the king.

'That's very rough play,' Fergus said.

'They started it,' the boy said, 'they didn't make me welcome.'

'No one can play with the boy troop unless they ask for special leave and protection,' Conchobor said.

'I didn't know that,' Setanta said, 'or I would have asked for it.'

'Well then,' Conchobor said, 'you had better tell us your name.'

'Setanta, son of Sualtim and Dechtire,' the child replied.

11

Conchobor's face broke into a huge smile. 'You should always make yourself known,' he said, 'it saves a lot of trouble.' He brought his nephew out to the boys on the lawn and asked them to let him join the troop. Then there was peace on the lawns of Emain Macha and Setanta stayed in the palace and all the chiefs of Ulster helped to bring him up.

In Ulster at that time there was a great smith called Culainn who was organising a special feast for Conchobor and the men of Ulster. On the day of the feast Conchobor passed by the lawn where his young nephew was playing with the boy troop. Setanta had the ball and he ran and weaved his way through the others and won the goal. It seemed impossible to defeat him.

'That boy will serve Ulster yet,' Conchobor said to Amergin. 'Go and call him and we'll take him to the feast with us.'

The child came running up, slightly out of breath, when he was called. 'I can't leave the game,' he said, when Amergin told him about the feast, 'the boys aren't finished yet.'

'Kings do not wait upon games,' Conchobor said, dryly.

'Then I will follow you,' Setanta said, 'by the chariot tracks.'

Conchobor laughed and waved him away. 'Go back to the hurling,' he said, 'there will be time enough for feasts when you are older.'

Culainn, the smith, made the king and his men very welcome. Fresh rushes were laid on the floor. The poets and musicians were there to greet them and after a while food was brought into the guests.

'Are we all here?' Culainn asked the king.

'We are,' Conchobor said, forgetting what the little boy had said about following him. 'Why do you ask?'

'Because I have a fierce hound which has the strength of a hundred. He won't let anyone near the house or land and I don't want to let him off the chain if more of your people are coming.'

'There's no one else,' Conchobor said. 'Loose the hound, he will protect us while we enjoy ourselves.'

The smith went and let the dog off his chain. The dog stretched himself and growled and then made a circuit of the whole neighbourhood and came back to lie in his usual place, just outside the house. Everyone was careful to keep away from him; he was the most savage dog ever known.

Eventually the games on the lawn at Emain Macha came to an end and all the boys went home for their evening meal. Setanta remembered the feast and went in search of the chariot tracks. As usual he shortened the journey by throwing his ball and his dart and hurrying forward to catch them. He heard the sound of laughter and feasting from some distance away and he smiled to himself, pleased that he had found the house so easily.

The hound heard him coming and began to roar and howl so much that he could be heard throughout Ulster. He sprang at the child as if he was going to swallow him in one bite. The boy's only weapons, if weapons they were, were the stick and ball. When he saw the hound coming at him he thrust the ball down the animal's throat so hard that it went right through his body. Then he picked up the dog by the hind legs and dashed him to pieces against a rock.

The men of Ulster had heard the noise and they came rushing out. Conchobor had remembered the child and he was afraid of what he might find.

'My sister's child,' he shouted. 'The hound will have killed him! I should have brought him with me...'

The men jumped through windows and over walls in their haste. Fergus was the first out. He saw the dead dog and the unconcerned child and he began to laugh with relief. He swung the boy up on his shoulder and brought him safely into the smith's house. Only the smith was upset. He went outside and saw his dead hound, who had been so faithful to him and obeyed only him. There were tears in his eyes as he touched the broken body. He crouched down,

13

holding the dog for a while and then went back angrily into the house.

'There is no welcome for you here,' he said to the child.

'Why not?' asked Conchobor.

'It was bad luck that brought him here and that made me invite you all. Now I have no one to protect my flocks and my herds. I'm going to lose everything. I may as well give up.' He bent his head, 'that dog,' he said, in a low voice, 'was like a member of my own family.'

'Then I will make it up to you,' Setanta said.

'How can you do that?' the king asked.

'I will find a whelp of the same breed and I will rear him and train him until he is as fierce and as obedient as the one I've killed.'

'That will take years,' said the smith.

'Then in the meantime I'll watch your cattle and your land.'

'That's a fair offer,' Conchobor said to the smith.

The smith considered for a moment. 'Very well,' he replied, 'if you can do it, then I accept.'

'And we will call you Cuchulainn, the Hound of Culainn,' said Cathbad the Druid, 'and one day your name will be on the lips of every man in the world.'

'I prefer my own name of Setanta,' the child answered. There was no doubt that he had a mind of his own.

'Setanta will never be famous,' Cathbad said.

The child stared at him and then said, 'in that case you may call me Cuchulainn.'

THE WOOING OF EMER

Cuchulainn came to manhood almost overburdened with gifts. He was handsome, gentle, sweet of tongue, skilled in every feat and very wise. When he fought he controlled his temper and matched his opponent with intelligence and sword play, until his battle fury came on him and then he shone with a hero-light and performed miracles of strength. He could joust and balance and was marvellous with horses. He defeated all his opponents at chess and draughts; he could count more quickly than the pursekeepers and, with a rod in his hand, divined water where none had ever been known. Above all that he had great judgement.

Needless to say all the women of Ulster adored him. The men, however, had a few reservations. He had three main faults, they felt: he was too young and boyish-looking, which made men who did not know him unable to take him seriously; he was too daring and he was much too beautiful. But time, they felt, would take care of most of that, and in the meantime, the men of Ulster thought it best to find him a wife.

'It will stop our own womenfolk making so much of him,' said one anxious young husband feelingly.

'He must have an heir,' said another, who had taken the precaution of locking up his daughters. 'The druids say he will die young.'

'Very well,' Conchobor said. 'I will send messengers to every corner of Ireland to find the daughter of a king or a great landowner who might please our young Hound.'

Nine stewards went from the court and they spent a whole year visiting every province of Ireland but they could not find a young girl to please Cuchulainn. In any case, he

15

had already made up his mind. The girl he wanted was Emer, the daughter of Forgall Manach the Wily, and so he yoked his chariot and called Loeg, his driver, and went out himself to court her. He had dressed himself carefully in a rich crimson five-folded tunic with a white-hooded shirt embroidered with gold thread and a silken cloak fastened with an inlaid brooch. He was a magnificent sight as he drove across the country to Luglochta Loga and Forgall's dún.

Cuchulainn chose Emer because she had the six gifts which were most important in his eyes: beauty, softness of voice, sweetness of words, skill in needlework, wisdom and, above all, chastity. In addition she matched him in age and appearance and nobility of birth and he had always said that his wife would have to have all these things.

Cuchulainn found Emer sitting on the lawn outside her father's house, showing the daughters of neighbouring landowners how to do fine embroidery. They heard him coming while he was still some distance away. There was the clatter of hooves, the snorting of hard-driven horses, the creaking and cracking of harnesses and chariot wheels.

'Will someone go and see who is coming?' Emer said, looking up briefly from her needlework. Her sister got up and went out to meet the stranger, and brought him over to the young girls.

'I come in friendship,' Cuchulainn said.

Emer raised her lovely face and they gazed at each other for a long moment.

'May the Gods smooth every path before you,' she said.

'And you,' he replied, in his gentle voice, 'may they always protect you.'

'Where did you come from?' she asked wonderingly.

Cuchulainn glanced around quickly. The look that had passed between them had made their feelings plain and Emer's friends were crowding round to listen to every word they said. Cuchulainn smiled at Emer and answered her questions in riddles.

'I came from Intide Emna,' he said.

'Where did you sleep?' Emer asked.

'In the house of a man who tends the cattle at Tethra.'

'What did you eat?' she asked.

'A broken chariot was cooked for me,' he said.

'Which way did you travel?'

'Between the mountains and the woods,' Cuchulainn answered.

'And after that?'

'An easy route,' he said, 'by the Cover of the Sea and over the Secret Places of the Dé Dananns and the Foam of the Horses of Emain; over the Great Sow's Back and the Valley of the Great Dam, between God and his Druid; over the Marrow of the Woman, between the Boar and the Dam, over the Washing-place of the Horse of Dea; around the Four Corners of the World, over the Remnants of the Great Feast...'

Emer smothered a smile, 'but who are you?' she asked.

'I am the nephew of a man who disappears in another in the wood of Badb,' said Cuchulainn.

'I see,' said Emer.

'And you?' Cuchulainn asked, 'It is your turn to give an account of yourself.'

'What should a maiden be,' Emer asked, 'but Teamhair upon the hills, a watcher that sees no one, an eel hiding in the water, a rush out of reach? The daughter of a king,' she went on, 'is a flame of hospitality but a road which cannot be entered. I have champions who follow me everywhere to make sure that no one takes me against my will, or against my father's wishes.'

'Tell me their names,' said Cuchulainn.

'Two called Lui, two by the name of Luath, the sons of Tethra, Brion, Bolor, Triath...'

'How many?' Cuchulainn demanded.

'A hundred,' Emer said, 'and each with the strength of another hundred and the feats of nine more. My father is stronger than any mighty smith and wiser than the most

17

learned druid and quicker of thought than any poet. You will have more than games to do,' she said, looking at him hard, 'to overcome him.'

'You do not think I am strong enough?' he asked.

'If your doings were well known, perhaps I would,' she said.

'By my oath,' Cuchulainn said, 'I will make them known. My name will be talked of with heroes.'

'Tell me how strong you are?' she said.

'I can easily do that,' Cuchulainn said. 'When I am at my weakest I can defend twenty others, a third of my strength is like that of thirty men and in my full prime I can fight alone against forty. A hundred are safe under my protection,' he said, getting into his stride, 'and brave warriors avoid meeting me at bridges and in battles. Armies retreat from me...'

'That is not bad for a youth,' Emer said, 'but you are not yet a chariot chief.'

'I have been brought up by Conchobor,' Cuchulainn said, stung. 'I am not a country boy, but the son of a royal princess. All the chiefs, heroes, druids and learned men of Ulster have taught me their gifts.'

'Who are they, then?' Emer asked, 'these who have taught you the things you are boasting about?'

'Sencha taught me wisdom and judgement,' Cuchulainn said, 'and Blai took me into his mighty house where we entertained all the great men of Ulster; Fergus taught me to fight and Amergin the Poet gave me the art of conversation. Cathbad the Druid gave me the druid arts and all the men of Ulster have had a hand in bringing me up, chariot drivers, poets, kings and chiefs alike. 'I am,' he said, with a notice-able lack of modesty, 'the darling of the whole army.' He paused and then asked, sharply, 'how were you brought up?'

Emer was taken aback but she rallied quickly.

'In ancient virtues,' she said, 'lawful behaviour, chastity and stateliness of form as befits a queen and in every noble way known to the women of Ireland.'

'They are excellent virtues,' Cuchulainn said. 'Above all, you are the first young girl I've met who could stand up to me in talk. Is there any reason,' he asked, 'that we should not become one?'

'Perhaps you have a wife already?' Emer said.

'Indeed I have not,' Cuchulainn replied, which was not entirely true, because he had already known many women.

'But whether you have or not is of no consequence,' Emer said, 'because I may not marry before my older sister.'

'I haven't fallen in love with your sister,' Cuchulainn said, 'I've fallen in love with you.' His eyes fell to her round swelling breasts above the line of her dress and his voice thickened. 'They are beautiful,' he said, 'it is the fairest sweetest plain in the land.'

'No one comes to this plain,' Emer said, 'who has not overcome a hundred warriors on every ford from Ailbine to Banchuig.'

'The softest, most tender plain...' Cuchulainn said, stretching out his hand. Emer moved back. 'No one comes to this plain,' she said, 'who does not go out safely from Smahain to Oilmell, and to Beltaine and to Bron Trogain.'

'Is that what you command me to do?' Cuchulainn asked.

'It is,' Emer said, 'and after that I will accept your offer.'

They spoke no more about it but both knew a pact had been made and Cuchulainn left shortly afterwards. As he drove away, Loeg, his chariot-driver, asked him about the riddles.

'Did you think I wanted all her maidens to know I had come courting her?' Cuchulainn asked. 'They would go straight to Forgall and tell him what we planned.'

'But what did all those words mean?' Loeg asked.

'When I told her I came from Intide Emna,' Cuchulainn said, patiently, 'she knew I meant Emain Macha, which took its name from Macha the daughter of Aed the Red. The sons of Dithorba fought her for the kingship when her father died and she defeated them and made them into her servants and forced them to dig a rath for her, which she marked out with the gold pin from her neck. Emain Macha: a brooch in the neck of Macha.'

'I hope it was clearer to Emer than it is to me,' Loeg replied.

'She would know that the man who tends the cattle at Tethra is Ronca the fisherman of Conchobor, because he catches fishes under the sea and fish are the cattle of the sea, and the sea is the plain of Tethra, a king of the Fomors.'

'Is that so?' said Loeg.

'And the ruins of a chariot was obviously a foal that was cooked for me on the hearth.'

'Obviously,' said Loeg.

'The mountains and the woods were Slieve Fuad in the west and Slieve Cullin to the east and the wood of Oircil between the two.'

'And the Cover of the Sea?' Loeg asked.

'The Plain of Muirthemne of course,' Cuchulainn said. 'It takes its name from the magic sea that was once there and the sea turtle that sucked men down to their death, and the Secret Places of the Dé Dananns and the Foam of the Horses is the magic place of the *Sidhe*. They reared two horses there and a bright stream flowed from them over the land and that water was called Uanib which is the name of the place to this day.'

'Emer would know that?' Loeg asked.

'She would certainly know the Great Sow's back,' Cuchulainn said. 'It is the ridge of Bregin, shaped like a sow, which appeared every time the Dé Dananns cast a spell.'

'And the Valley of the Great Dam between God and his Druid?'

'Angus Og of the Sidhe,' Cuchulainn replied impatiently, 'and his Druid to the west of the Brugh. Between them was one woman, the wife of the smith and that is the way I went, between those hills. The Marrow of the Woman,' he went on, 'is the Boinne, and it gets its name from Boann the wife of Nechtan. She was warned not to go to the hidden well at the bottom of their *dún* without three cup bearers to protect her, or she would get a blemish, but she went alone with a queen's pride and passed left-hand-wise around the well to mock its powers and, as a result, bruised her two knees, her right hand and one of her eyes and she ran out of the *dún* to escape and the water followed her wherever she went. Segain is the name of that place.'

'I hope Emer knows these old stories as well as you do,' Loeg said.

'She does,' Cuchulainn said, 'I am sure of it.' He paused for a moment. 'The Boar and the Dam,' he continued, 'is between Cleitech and Fessi. Cleitech is the name of a boar, but it is also the name for a king, and the Washing Place of the Horses of Dea is Ange, because that is where the Tuatha dé Dananns washed their horses.'

'Yes, I did know that,' Loeg said.

'The Four Corners of the World is Muincille where Mann the farmer made spells in the great four-cornered chambers under the ground to keep the plague from the cattle in the time of Bresel, the king of Leinster. The Remnants of the Great Feast was of course Tailne, where a great banquet was given to Lugh after the battle of Magh Tuireadh.'

'That's all very well,' Loeg said, 'but where is the Wood of Badb and what did Emer mean by all her talk?'

'The Wood of Badb is the land of Ross and I am a river which mixes with another called Conchobor. I am of his blood and his nephew. And as for Emer...'

'Yes?' said Loeg.

'She said that no man could come to the plain of her breasts...'

'Yes?' said Loeg again, but Cuchulainn was thinking about Emer's breasts and he didn't answer for some time.

'She meant,' Cuchulainn said, eventually, sighing with the memory, 'that I must kill a hundred men with one blow but save one man in nine, that means that I must spare her brothers and then I must carry her foster-sister and herself with their share of gold and silver out of the *dún* of Forgall.'

21

'I don't know how you got all that from what she said,' Loeg grumbled.

'I must fight the length of one year, because Samhain is the end of summer; Oimell the beginning of spring; Beltaine is the time of fires, when the druids used to make spells to drive out the cattle; Bron Trogain is the autumn, when the earth is in labour under the harvest. So I suggest,' Cuchulainn said, sharply, 'that you whip up the horses because I have a great deal to do and there are hard times in front of us.' So Loeg drove the rest of the way at a furious pace and in silence.

When Forgall came back to his *dún* with his local lords, their daughters told him about the handsome young man who had arrived in such style and had spent so much time talking to Emer.

'But we couldn't understand what they were saying,' one girl said. 'It was all about Gods and druids and ancient battles.'

'It's that mad boy from Emain Macha, I know it!' Forgall shouted. 'He's been here to court Emer and she is young enough and silly enough to have fallen in love with him. He thinks he can come here and mystify me with riddles, but I'll show him what I can do. There will be no marriage between our houses.' Forgall called his men and they set out for Emain Macha almost immediately but Forgall went disguised as a foreigner and pretended that he was the king of Gall with his courtiers. He paid homage to Conchobor and presented him with precious gifts and wine from Gall and they received a great welcome from the Ulster king. The feasting went on for three days and Conchobor showed off all his best warriors to the visiting royals. Cuchulainn and Conall, above all, were singled out for praise.

'Wonderful feats,' murmured Forgall, from the royal stand, 'and the young man is the finest of them all.'

After the games Forgall asked to speak to Cuchulainn and Conchobor called him over.

'You are, without doubt, the most skilled champion that I have ever seen,' Forgall said, silkily, 'but there is a wise woman, a warrior in her own right, in the east of Alban who could teach you such skills that no one could ever match you.'

'Then he must go there!' Conchobor said, heartily, and Cuchulainn smiled and thanked the so-called king of Gall.

'But he won't return alive,' Forgall thought to himself, 'not if I have anything to do with it. The people around Scathach are fierce and I will make the road even more dangerous than it is already.'

Cuchulainn set out for Alban with Laegaire and Conall but first he went to visit Emer and tell her his plans. 'That wasn't the king of Gall,' she said, alarmed, 'that was my father. He is determined to get rid of you. You must be very careful. He can do all kinds of spells and I know he will stop at nothing.'

'I will be careful,' Cuchulainn said, 'and will you be true to me until I return?'

'Only death would come between us,' Emer said, and Cuchulainn took her hands between his and then resolutely turned his face towards Alban and the ship which was waiting for him.

They landed safely, without incident, and spent a few days with Donall the smith before setting out to the east. When they had rested they started on the journey to the warrior-queen but, on the way, they saw a vision of Emain Macha. Forgall had arranged it and it was so life-like that Conall and Laegaire could not pass it. They turned back and Cuchulainn went on alone, which was exactly what Forgall wanted. Cuchulainn was sad for the road was strange and he missed his friends but he had given his word to Conchobor that he would go and learn Scathach's skills. He was determined to continue even if he should die in the attempt.

Soon he saw a huge, ferocious beast coming towards him. It looked rather like a lion and it growled and watched him from the edge of a wood. Cuchulainn took another path but the beast changed its route too and followed him. Which ever way Cuchulainn tried to go the animal went the same way so, in the end, Cuchulainn got tired of being tracked and took a great leap on to the animal's back and let the beast lead the way. They travelled for four days until they came to a lake with an island on it and men rowing in a boat. The men laughed at the sight of Cuchulainn on the strange beast's back, so he jumped off and the lion-like creature slunk away into the bushes. Cuchulainn never saw him again, much to Forgall's annoyance. He continued on foot and came to a house in a valley where a young girl spoke to him.

'Welcome Cuchulainn,' she said.

'How do you know me?' he asked.

'I was in the house of Wulfkin the Saxon when you came here to learn sweet speech from him,' she replied. She gave him food and drink and sent him on his way refreshed. On the road he met a young man who also welcomed him.

'I am better known than I thought,' Cuchulainn said to himself, as he inquired the way to Scathach's house.

'That is the Plain of Ill-Luck,' the young man said. 'At this side your feet will stick to the grass and at the other the grass will rise and hold you on its points. Take this wheel,' he went on, 'it will lead you across the first half.'

'Then what do I do?' Cuchulainn asked.

The young man gave him an apple. 'Throw that and follow it and you'll get across safely.'

'I am very grateful to you,' Cuchulainn said and the young man smiled, wished him luck and warned him of all the other pitfalls he might meet.

'But you will get through,' he said, 'and be famous for it.'

Cuchulainn crossed the plain exactly as the young man had told him and then came to a narrow valley full of monsters. The young man wasn't exaggerating, Cuchulainn thought, as he made his way through the one narrow path in the valley. After that there was a fierce, wild mountain but eventually he came to some houses and met Scathach's scholars and with them Ferdiad son of Daman and the three sons of Usnach. They made him welcome and kissed him and asked about Ireland.

'Scathach is over there on that island,' Ferdiad said, when they had exchanged all their news. 'You must go by the bridge on the cliff but before that you must prove yourself a champion.' Ferdiad shook his head and continued, 'many a king's son has lost his life on that cliff.'

It was no ordinary bridge. The ends of it were low and the middle very steep. When anyone stepped on it for the first time the centre narrowed to the narrowness of a human hair; the second time it would shorten to the shortness of an inch; the third time it would become as slippery as an eel but the fourth time, it would rear itself up into the air until it was as tall as the mast of a ship.

There was, needless to say, a great crowd assembled to see Cuchulainn make the attempt to cross it. He tried three times but between the narrowness and the shortness and the slipperiness of it, he was still trapped at the same side. The people on the lawns were laughing at him.

'He's a bit young to be trying what others have attempted to do for years,' one man said and Cuchulainn heard him. His battle anger came on him, the hero-light shone around his head and he took on the appearance of a god. He jumped on to the bridge and made a great leap like a salmon. He touched the middle of the bridge so lightly that he was up again at the other side before the bridge could rear itself up. He was on the lawn outside Scathach's house almost before the watching crowd could raise a cheer.

The house had seven huge doors and seven windows between each door and three times fifty beautiful young girls in scarlet cloaks waiting on the warrior-queen. It was a magnificent sight and Cuchulainn stood, for a moment, just gazing at the great house. He was almost unaware that he was an equally magnificent sight himself but Scathach's daughter, Uacthach, saw him from the window and she

25

thought he was the most handsome man in the world. She had watched him cross the bridge with his hero's leap and she fell in love with him at first sight. Her colour came and went with excitement and she put silver threads in her needlework where gold ones should go, and gold threads in the place of silver ones. Scathach, who missed nothing, looked across at her and said dryly, 'I think the young man pleases you.'

'I hope he will return alive to his own people,' Uacthach said, 'because there must be someone whose heart would break if he did not.'

Cuchulainn marched up to the door and banged so hard on it with his spear that the point went straight through it.

'This young man must have already finished his training,' Scathach said to her daughter, 'you had better let him in.'

Uacthach went to Cuchulainn and told him where to find her mother and whispered a few words of advice to him. Cuchulainn listened and nodded and then went out to the garden where Scathach was teaching her two sons. Cuchulainn took out his sword and put its point between the warrior-queen's breasts and threatened her with a slow and painful death if she did not teach him all he wanted to know.

'Very well,' she said, 'but I think you have very little to learn.'

Cuchulainn was not the only one at that time who was looking for a wife. While he was in Alban with Scathach, Lugaid, king of Munster, went searching Ireland for a wife, taking with him his twelve chariot chiefs. Forgall heard about this and went immediately to Emain Macha to find Lugaid and guide his steps to his own *dún*.

'I have the best of daughters,' he told the Munster king. 'She is beautiful and graceful and skilled in needlework and you may have her as your wife. Not only that,' he said, 'there are twelve daughters of twelve lords of Bregia who will do very nicely for your twelve chariot chiefs.' So Lugaid was brought to Bregia and a great wedding feast was arranged. But Forgall had reckoned without Emer. She went to meet Lugaid, as her father asked, and he came to sit beside her. She took his face between her hands and stared at him.

'I have promised myself to Cuchulainn,' she said, 'and I have promised on my good name and on my life, even though my father hates him. No honourable man should force me to become his wife.'

'Of all the men in Ireland,' Lugaid said, feelingly, 'I will not fight Cuchulainn. You may keep your promise to him.' He left the *dún* sadly and went back to his lands in Munster.

Cuchulainn was still in Alban with Scathach. A war had broken out between herself and Aoife, another warrior-queen. Scathach was trying to keep Cuchulainn quiet and out of harm's way with a sleeping draught because she knew that he couldn't resist a fight and she was afraid of Aoife's magic powers. But she didn't know Cuchulainn's strength. The sleeping draught, which would have kept any ordinary man unconscious for a day and a night, kept him asleep for only an hour. Then he got up and went to fight Aoife, taking with him Scathach's two sons.

They met the warrior-queen and Cuchulainn killed Aoife's three champions, one after the other, but the battle wasn't over. Three other champions were lined up for the next day and Scathach was afraid for her two sons. She need not have been. Once again Cuchulainn went ahead and killed the three champions before anyone else in Scathach's army could get to them.

'I call on Scathach to fight with me herself!' Aoife demanded.

'I will go in your place,' Cuchulainn replied and asked, 'what does she think most of in the world?'

'Her chariot,' Scathach said, 'and her driver and the two horses.'

Cuchulainn nodded, 'I'll remember that,' he said.

'You may have need to,' Scathach told him.

It was not the easy fight that Cuchulainn had expected. Aoife was a formidable warrior and before long she had broken Cuchulainn's spear in pieces and snapped his sword off at the hilt.

'Look!' Cuchulainn shouted suddenly, 'your horses and the chariot and the driver have fallen into the valley!' It wasn't a very original ploy but it worked: Aoife looked around and lost her advantage. Cuchulainn had her on the ground in seconds. He put his sword to her breast with all her army looking on and she was ashamed.

'Are you going to kill me?' she asked.

'Not if you make peace with Scathach,' Cuchulainn said.

'Very well,' said the warrior-queen, 'but if it was any other man,' she said, suddenly, her magnificent eyes flashing, 'I would rather die than give in.'

Cuchulainn put his sword on one side and lifted her up to face him.

'You are a very brave woman,' he said, 'and a beautiful one.'

'And I have met my match,' she replied, 'in more ways than one.'

Cuchulainn moved into her palace with her. She took him to her bed and gave him all her love but neither of them knew that this was the beginning of the greatest tragedy of Cuchulainn's life.

As he returned to Scathach he had another near-escape from death when he met an old hag on a narrow cliff path. She was the mother of three of the dead champions of Aoife and she was determined to have her revenge.

'Let me pass,' she demanded, knowing his rules of chivalry.

'I would, willingly,' he said, 'but it would mean throwing myself hundreds of feet down the cliff.'

'Let me pass,' she said again. 'You can hang on to the path with one hand.'

So Cuchulainn hung from the edge of the path and the hag came to pass him. As she did so she gave his hand a kick

28

but Cuchulainn made his great hero-leap and jumped back up on to the path and struck off the hag's head. So it was with this savage finality that he left Aoife's lands.

Scathach welcomed him back and continued to teach him until he had mastered all the arts of war and championship. Then Conchobor sent for him and Cuchulainn had to say goodbye.

'You will meet with great dangers,' Scathach said, she had the druid's gift of prophesy, 'you will fight great armies and scatter your enemies and your name will be heard even as far as here, but your life will not be long. You will die in the fullness of manhood.'

It was a sad leave-taking but Cuchulainn found his friends waiting for him on the other side of the bridge and together they set sail for Ireland. On the way they came to the island of Rechrainn and they landed there for the night. On the strand was a lovely young girl crying her eyes out.

'Who are you?' asked Cuchulainn, 'and what is the matter?'

'My name is Devorgill,' she said, 'and my father, the king, cannot pay his taxes to the Fomor monster and he has to leave me here so that the Fomor's men can take me away instead.'

'Where are these men coming from?' Cuchulainn asked.

'From a far country,' she replied, 'and I wouldn't advise you to be here when they come. They are very fierce. They will probably kill you.'

'I can't leave you here,' Cuchulainn said, 'we will wait and see what they do.'

Not long afterwards three strong, brutal Fomor men landed and made straight for the girl. Cuchulainn leaped on them from behind a rock and killed them one after the other. He himself was unhurt, except for a scratch on his arm, which the girl bound up.

'Come to my father's house with me,' she said, 'he will want to thank you himself.'

They got a great welcome at the palace. The king was

delighted to see his daughter safe and Cuchulainn found some of his friends from Emain Macha there before him. It was almost dusk and, when the girl looked around to point out to her father which man had saved her, she found it hard to recognise Cuchulainn.

'It was me,' one of the men of Ulster said and some of the others shouted that it was one of them. Cuchulainn said nothing but, when water was brought for them all to wash before the feast the girl saw the strip of cloth on his arm and she brought him to her father.

'I will give you my daughter as your wife,' the king said, in gratitude, 'and pay you a fine fortune too.'

'I have to go back to Ireland,' Cuchulainn said, 'I am sorry Devorgill, but I cannot stay here and be your husband.'

After the feast he set sail with his friends and went directly to Ireland where he told the whole story to Conchobor at Emain Macha. As soon as he had rested, he set out to see Emer.

Forgall, furious that Cuchulainn had survived his stay in Alban, had made his *dún* so secure that Cuchulainn could not get near the house. He circled it and camped nearby. He circled it again and again but months passed and he did not see Emer even once. One day, tired of his constant watch on Forgall's *dún*, Cuchulainn went down to the shore with Loeg, his chariot-driver, and with Lugaid. There were two birds flying low over the shore and Cuchulainn idly put a stone in his sling and hit one of the birds. The bird fell and the other bird landed with it. The three men ran over to find that they were not birds at all but two beautiful young girls. One of them was Devorgill who had come from her own country to find Cuchulainn and it was she who had been hit by the stone.

'It was an unkind thing to do to me,' she said. 'when I had come all this way to see you.'

Cuchulainn bent his head and sucked at the wound and sucked out the stone and the blood with it.

'It is cured,' she said as she looked at him under her lashes, 'husband.'

'I can't be your husband,' Cuchulainn said very firmly, 'I have drunk your blood.' He drew Lugaid forward. 'But here is a man who will care for you. I will give you to him.'

Devorgill looked at Lugaid of the Red Stripes and forgot about Cuchulainn straight away; Lugaid returned her love to such an extent that they were together all her life. When she died he died of grief and love for her.

The interlude had given Cuchulainn new energy to attack Forgall's *dún* again. He ordered his scythe-chariot and when he reached the castle he made his hero-leap and took three walls at the one time and then made three rushes at the men inside and killed eight in every nine, so that the three brothers of Emer were left alive. Forgall, trying to imitate the champion, made a great leap over the walls to escape and fell to his death in the courtyard.

Cuchulainn took Emer away from Bregia and with her he brought her foster-sister and their gold and silver, just as she had asked him to that first day. But they were not quite free yet. Forgall's sister, Scenmend, pursued them and so they made a stand at the ford where Cuchulainn killed her in the fight. Afterwards it was called the Ford of Scenmend. Her men pursued him again and he killed a hundred at the next ford.

'We will call this the Ford of the Deeds,' Emer said. 'You are without doubt a great warrior.'

He had to fight again at Raeban, the white field, and streams of blood reddened the hills around.

'You have made it a hill of red sods,' Emer said, and from that time it has been called the Ford of the Sods.

They were overtaken again at the Boinne and Emer fled from the chariot while Cuchulainn killed all about him along the banks of the river and huge clods of earth were thrown north and south across the water from the hooves of the horses.

'You have kept your word and killed a hundred,' Emer

said, when it was safe to come back to the chariot. 'We will call it the Ford of the Two Clods.'

'I have brought you safely through it all,' Cuchulainn said, as he brought her home in triumph to Emain Macha.

He was given a hero's welcome and made leader of the young men of Ulster, head of the warriors, head of the poets, head of the musicians and the pipers and even the jesters. The poets said that when the young men of Ireland were in the Palace of the Red Branch of Ulster they were the fairest of the fair, but Cuchulainn was hard and steel bright and the fairest of them all.

The king himself gave Emer a great welcome and all the chief men of Ulster were glad to greet her.

'After all the hardships and the long courting,' Conchobor said, 'you will be married here in my palace and live at the side of Cuchulainn your whole lives long.'

THE WEAKNESS OF THE MEN OF ULSTER

When Maeve, queen of Connacht, decided to go to war on Ulster in order to kidnap the brown bull, the famous Donn Cualnge, she consulted a druid to find out the result of the forthcoming battles. Feidelm, the prophetess, did not tell Maeve exactly what she wanted to hear. She foretold that Maeve would survive the war, which was pleasant enough news but, when pressed, repeatedly chanted, 'I see red, I see crimson.'

Maeve pointed out that Conchobor, the king of Ulster, was ill; Mac Comchobuir was laid low; Mac Durthach had retired to Rath Airthir — in fact, that the men of Ulster were suffering from their usual sickness.

'We have nothing to fear from Ulster,' she said.

'I see red, I see crimson,' Feidelm replied, 'and I see it on your armies.'

'You know about the curse on the Ulster warriors,' Maeve asked, lifting her head and glaring at the prophetess.

'Of course,' Feidelm said.

Maeve bit back a sharp retort. The forecast of woe had gone on for far too long but it was never wise to offend a prophetess.

'And their sickness?' she asked.

'Everyone knows about that,' Feidelm replied.

It was, indeed, well-known that Ulstermen often faltered in battle. The cause was a curse, the seeds of which had been sown, harmlessly enough, when the wife of a moderately prosperous man called Crunden, had died.

Crunden, son of Agnoman, lived fairly well on his land but it was a quiet place in the mountains and he was lonely. He also had to care for his children without a woman to help him and he couldn't do that properly as well as tend to the land. But one day a stranger came. All that Crunden saw, when he answered her knock, was a tall, beautiful woman but in reality she was the goddess Macha.

She walked in as though she knew both him and the house and, in spite of her good clothes, sat down by the fire and kindled it. Then she went to find some meal and mixed some bread. She did all this without saying a word and Crunden watched her in amazement. When evening came she went out and milked the cows. She prepared some food for the family and stayed up until everyone was settled for the night. Then, and only then, did she rekindle the fire again and take a rest.

She stayed on in the house and it seemed the most natural thing in the world. Crunden married her and she looked after him and his sons and was in every way an exemplary wife. Things went so well for Crunden, now that he was able to tend to his land, that he felt he could spare the time to go to the big fair which was being organised for the whole of Ulster. There were to be games and races and trading of cattle. Huge crowds were expected.

'Don't go,' said Crunden's new wife.

'But why?' he asked.

'Because if you so much as speak my name you will lose me forever.'

'Which you know I would never want to do', as he bent to give her a kiss. 'I'd like to go,' he said, wistfully.

Her face softened. 'I understand that,' she said, 'but what I say is true. You mustn't talk about me there.'

'I promise you I won't,' said Crunden.

He set out jauntily when the day came but his wife stood in the doorway and watched him go with a sad face.

It was a very entertaining gathering. Crunden travelled there with a group of friends and together they talked and laughed. They watched the amusements, listened to the strolling players, enjoyed the music and the noise as well all the raucous life of the fair. A few hours later the royal

34

chariot arrived and the king's horses won the most important race. The bards and the poets immediately started to compose songs and verses in praise of the royal party and the king's servants shouted that there were no better horses in Ireland than those of their master, and no better runners in the whole country.

Crunden had been indulging himself a little too much.

'My wife is a better runner than those two horses,' he cried. He was of the opinion that his wife was superior in all things to everyone and everything else.

'Get hold of that man,' the king said, when the story was whispered to him, 'and we'll keep him here until we can try out his wife against the horses.'

Crunden was grabbed by rough hands and brought to the king.

'Where do you live?' the king asked and Crunden, frightened out of his wits by the sight of the king and the rough handling of the servants, told him.

A short time later Crunden's wife was surprised to see royal messengers coming towards the house.

'Welcome', she said, 'but what brings you here?'

'You do,' they said, 'we have come to bring you to the king, by his own order.'

'To the king?' she asked.

'At the fair,' they said, 'where the king is waiting to see you run faster than his horses.'

'But —' the woman began.

'Your husband said you could,' the servant said. By now he had a firm grip on her arm, 'and he is to be kept a prisoner until you come to release him.'

The woman sighed. 'I told him not to talk about me. You must see that I am about to give birth to a child — how can I run against the king's horse, or any horse for that matter? Crunden was very stupid . . . ' she said, her voice rising.

'He will soon be very dead if you do not come,' the servant said.

She lifted her shoulders in an expression of despair, 'then I will have to go'.

She spoke quietly to the children and then told the men that she was ready. One of them lifted her in front of him on to his horse and they went back as quickly as they could. Word had got around and half Ulster was there to meet her. She held her head in shame.

'How can they look at me the way I am?' she said, 'and why have you brought me here?'

'You know why,' the messenger said as he set her down on the ground.

'You are here to run against the king's two horses,' the crowd shouted.

'But my time has almost come,' she said.

She was taken, protesting, to the king.

'Take out your sword,' the king said to his chief servant, 'and put the husband of this defiant woman to death.'

'Help me!' the woman screamed to the crowd, 'everyone of you was born of a mother.'

'Kill him,' the king said, implacably.

She knelt down at his feet, 'at least wait until my child is born...'

'It is fair day,' the king said. 'How can we wait?'

'If I am to be shamed before all these people' Macha said, 'there will be even more shame on you.'

'We are waiting,' the king said.

'Have you no pity?' Crunden's wife asked.

'Your husband made a boast,' the king said, 'and if he can't justify it, then he has to be punished. We are not to be mocked,' he added.

'How can I mock you?' the woman asked.

'Bring on the horses,' the king ordered.

'If my husband is going to be punished,' the woman screamed out, 'you will be punished even more!'

The king snapped his fingers: 'The horses.'

'Bring them,' Macha said, suddenly calm, 'but at your own risk!'

'I had not thought,' the king remarked, behind his hand to the queen, 'that we would have such an amusing day.'

The queen did not reply because she remembered her own hours in childbed.

Crunden struggled to get away from the soldiers but they held on to him with grips of iron. He gave his wife a look which was a mixture of shame and anguish but she didn't meet his eyes. She was sweating as she knelt at the starting line. She lifted her head up once to look at the royal party. Only the queen looked away.

'Try not to spoil everything for me,' the king said to his consort, in a bored voice.

A voice shouted and the race began. The woman streaked forward from her starting position and kept up well with the two horses. At one point, about a third of the way, she stumbled and doubled up with pain. The horses went ahead and then the woman dragged herself to her feet, gave one quick backward glance at Crunden, then made a supreme effort and passed the two horses just before the finishing line. She fell there and screamed in agony. Her hair was plastered to her head and her face twisted in pain.

The king felt curiously tired. 'She won,' he said and turned away. 'It was not as amusing as I had hoped. Get the chariot ready. We are leaving.' He waved a hand in the direction of Crunden, 'and you'd better let him go.'

The charioteers tried to catch the horses without much success.

'My legs have gone,' one said. He had a very surprised expression on his face as his knees slowly buckled under him.

The woman screamed again. Her time had come and Crunden hurried over to help her. Her shrieks rent the air and she gave birth to two children, a boy and a girl. With her last cry every man in the crowd felt his strength suddenly leaving him and, as the wails of the newly born increased in volume, the men of Ulster were drained of every bit of energy they had. The woman lay on the ground at the finishing post with her two infants beside her. 'From this day on,' she said, scarcely able to whisper, 'and until the ninth generation...' she raised her head slightly and the king, who was dragging himself with great difficulty towards his chariot, felt the skin on the back of his neck go cold as he turned to look at the woman. 'Until the ninth generation,' the woman said, taking on the appearance of the goddess, Macha, 'the shame that you have brought to me today will fall on you. When you most need your strength, when your enemies are closing in on you, the weakness of a woman in childbirth will come upon every man in Ulster and it will last until the battle is over.'

Maeve repeated this story to Feidelm, amending it slightly to show the royals involved in a better light. 'That is exactly what happened, and every Ulster man born after that is under the curse.'

'But not those born before it was uttered,' Feidelm said.

'No,' Maeve admitted, 'but they are all old now.'

'There is one other exception,' Feidelm replied. 'I have told you of the great hero coming shining out of Ulster.'

'Over and over again,' Maeve said, irritably, 'I am sick of the name of Cuchulainn.'

'He is stronger than all the men in Ulster put together,' the prophetess warned, 'and has powers more magical than those of the goddess Macha. He does not suffer from the Ulster sickness.'

But Maeve ignored her advice and went ahead with the war. She was roundly defeated by Cuchulainn and driven back, humiliated, into Connacht.

CONLAOCH, SON OF AOIFE

Sometime after Cuchulainn and Aoife, the warrior-queen, became lovers she discovered that she was with child. Cuchulainn gave her a gold ring and asked her to keep it until the child grew to be a young man. He was sure it would be a boy.

'When his thumb is big enough for the ring,' he said, 'send him to Ireland so that I will know he is my son.'

'I promise,' Aoife replied. She was too proud a queen to ask him to stay; in any case she had sensed his restlessness from the beginning. He had killed her champions and he had won her with sweet words and his man's body. She loved him too much to tie him to the soft life at court.

'What name shall I give our son?' she asked, 'so that you will be sure to know him. Rings are sometimes lost.'

'Not the one I give you, surely?' Cuchulainn said. 'Do you like the name Conlaoch?'

Aoife considered it for a moment. 'Yes,' she replied, 'that is a fine name for a prince.'

So Cuchulainn left her and went back to Ireland and, although Aoife was sad, she had the child to look forward to and warm memories to treasure all her life. The child was a boy and she named him Conlaoch as Cuchulainn had asked. He was a beautiful baby, strong and well formed.

'Like a king's son,' she said to Scathach, the warrior-queen with whom she was now at peace, because of Cuchulainn's intervention. She smiled down at the child, 'when you are older,' she said, 'Scathach will teach you the arts of war as she taught your father.'

Unfortunately for Aoife, and for all of them as it turned out, Cuchulainn had already met Emer and he married her shortly afterwards. Bad news travels quickly and it wasn't long before it came to Aoife's ears. A woman scorned is a force to be reckoned with but for a queen to be set aside for another is to tempt all the fates beyond endurance.

'How could he?' Aoife said, storming around the palace 'He didn't even wait to see our child.'

'Ireland is far away and he has his life to live,' Scathach answered.

'It may be far,' the queen said, 'but I will have my revenge.'

'How?' Scathach asked, 'your champions are dead.'

'I have a son,' Aoife said, 'and I can wait.'

She brought up Conlaoch as a king's son and told him nothing of how she had been betrayed. When he was old enough she asked Scathach to teach him the use of arms and Conlaoch proved to be an apt pupil. He was as brave and as skilled as his father and Aoife was proud of him. She named him her champion and told him all that was expected of such a man.

'You must never give way to anyone,' she said.

'I won't,' Conlaoch replied.

'Even if it means your death?' Aoife demanded.

'Even if it means that,' Conlaoch said. He met her eyes in a steadfast gaze.

'And you must never refuse a challenge,' the queen said, however great the champion.'

'You need never fear that,' Conlaoch said.

'You will fight to the death?' Aoife asked.

'To the death,' he replied.

She smiled at him. 'There is one other thing, and this is the most important of all.'

'What could be more important than facing up to an enemy?' Conlaoch asked.

'You must never tell your name.'

Conlaoch stared at her. 'My name?'

'You may be threatened with all kinds of things, death even, but you must never, never say your name.'

'I don't understand,' Conlaoch said.

'I'm not asking you to understand,' Aoife said. She stood up and made an imperial gesture, 'I'm putting you under a solemn *geasa* not to fail me in any of these things.'

He fell to his knees, bowed his head and said, 'you have my solemn promise, and my bond.'

Aoife put her hands on his bent head and stared across the plain to the sea. She saw nothing but a red mist of anger and bitterness but when Conlaoch looked up she became conscious of his youth and beauty again and her heart faltered for a moment. Then the past flooded back and she saw Cuchulainn's face instead of her son's and the cold, implacable hatred returned.

She bade him farewell proudly, as a queen, and watched, dry-eyed, as his boat sailed. If afterwards she retired to her rooms and gave way to bitter tears no one, not even Scathach, knew of it. Conlaoch made landfall at Baile's Strand, near Dundealgan, Cuchulainn's home. He arrived at a time when Conchobor was holding court to settle some local business in the district. All the chiefs of Ulster were assembled when word was brought to the king of a fighting ship and armed men on the strand.

'Go to the leader and ask him who he is and why he has come here,' Conchobor said to Cuinaire, 'and bid him welcome if he has come as a friend.'

Cuinaire went down to the strand to meet Conlaoch. The messenger was relieved when he saw how young Conlaoch was and what an open, happy face he had.

'I think that since you are armed for fighting you must have been blown off course,' Cuinaire said. 'The king welcomes you to his court.'

'Thank you,' Conlaoch replied.

'You are from the east?' Cuinaire asked.

Conlaoch nodded, 'That is so.'

'Then tell me your name and your deeds and victories across the sea,' Cuinaire said.

'My name is of no importance to you,' the boy said,

'and in any case I am under oath not to tell it to a living soul.'

'Conchobor will not like that,' Cuinaire said, frowning.

'I cannot break my bond,' Conlaoch said.

'Many a champion from Alban and from Britain have met their death for refusing to give the king such a simple piece of information.'

'If that is your law then I shall have to break it,' Conlaoch said.

Cuinaire, troubled, went back to the king and told him what the boy had said. Conchobor was irritated, 'who will go out and show this young pup that he can't insult the High King?'

'I'll go,' Conall said, taking out his sword. Conchobor nodded, satisfied. Conall was always ready to defend Ulster and he was no mean champion; the matter was in safe hands.

Conall found Conlaoch some distance from the strand. The boy was angry and he and his men had already set about destroying houses and cattle. Conall rushed into the fray shouting and cursing and cutting the air with his sword. Conlaoch and Conall fought hard and long and eventually the younger man got the better of the Ulster champion. Conlaoch who looked down at Conall wounded on the ground said, 'now I have all the glory and praise that was due to you as a champion.'

One of Conall's men hurried away to Dundealgan to tell Cuchulainn what had happened.

'Conall has been humiliated,' the messenger said telling Cuchulainn the whole story, 'and we need the Hound of Ulster to help us.'

'Did you ever find me wanting?' Cuchulainn asked buckling on his weapons.

He found Conlaoch still angry and making further forays into Ulster territory. Conlaoch paused, though, when he saw the champion with the hero-light around him coming towards him. The boy held up his hand to halt his men and went to meet Cuchulainn. They took each other's measure for a moment and then Cuchulainn said, 'there is a way out of this. Just tell me who you are and why you have come and we can treat as friends and not enemies. Because if you do not,' he went on as Conlaoch began to refuse, 'I will have to fight you and I doubt if you will survive.'

Conlaoch put up his chin and his hand went to his sword.

'If I do to you what I did to Conall my name will be known the length and breadth of the kingdom.'

'If you put me down,' Cuchulainn said.

Conlaoch hesitated, 'if I draw back from the challenge my name will be a mockery.'

Cuchulainn seldom gave anyone a second chance but there was something nagging at the back of his mind, something that made him warm to this bright-faced boy.

'You have already defeated Conall,' he pointed out.

'So I am to bow the knee to you?' Conlaoch said.

'The king wants to know your name and business, that is all.'

'I will never give my name to anyone nor any account of myself,' Conlaoch shouted.

'No one questions your courage,' Cuchulainn said.

'I am under a *geasa*,' Conlaoch said more quietly, 'and perhaps if I were not, now that I have seen your face, I would tell you my name because you are truly the brave champion of Ireland.'

They stared at each other, the stallion and the young buck, and both knew that a fight was inevitable. The men of Ireland gathered to see the battle. It was a fight such as had seldom been seen before. Occasionally one or the other gained a slight advantage but then the situation was reversed and the crowd marvelled that the young man could hold out against Cuchulainn for so long and give the champion cause to worry.

Finally, after hours of fighting with neither conceding an inch, Conlaoch suddenly charged the Hound in a last burst of anger and speed. Cuchulainn realised that all the skills and stratagems which he possessed were also known to the young man and that there was a possibility of him losing the day to this stranger. So Cuchulainn called for the Gae-Bolga and his anger came on him and the hero-light burst into flames around his head and then, in that moment, Conlaoch recognised his father. He had been poised with his spear aimed directly at the champion but when he realised who it was he threw it to one side. But the Gae-Bolga had already left Cuchulainn's hand and it went straight through Conlaoch's body and the boy fell to the ground.

'Now,' Cuchulainn said, 'now tell me your name and where you come from and hurry, because you have little time left from that wound.'

Conlaoch stretched out his hand and showed Cuchulainn the ring on his thumb.

'My grief,' said Cuchulainn.

'Let my men come round me and see what revenge has done,' murmured the boy. 'Conlaoch is my name. I am the son of the Hound and...' Cuchulainn had to bend his head to hear the rest ... 'and heir to Dundealgan.'

'How?' Cuchulainn began, but the boy's hand was already cold in his own.

'I was bound to keep the secret,' Conlaoch whispered.

Cuchulainn took a deep breath. 'Your mother should be here to see this moment. She might have used her powers to stop my spear.'

'Twas she who bound me,' Conlaoch said as the strength returned briefly to his voice and he shouted in a voice like Cuchulainn's own, 'and I curse her!'

'I curse her too, I curse her a hundred and a hundred times!' Cuchulainn said. 'Why has she harboured this hatred and treachery all these years and brought this sorrow on us?'

'I gave my name to no man,' Conlaoch said his voice sinking, 'until now. I did not break my oath but, O Cuchulainn of the hero-light, it is a pity you did not know me when I sent my spear away from you in the fight.'

'You were the true champion,' Cuchulainn said, but Conlaoch did not hear him. His neck had arched in agony and Cuchulainn took his sword and ran it through him rather than have him suffer any longer. Tears fell from the Hound's eyes as he bent over his only son.

'Why did you come here, son of Aoife?' he asked in anguish. 'Why did you have to meet me of all the men of Ulster in a challenge.' He stroked the fair face, calm and beautiful again in death. 'We could have done such things together that not all the men of Ireland, from sea to sea, could have put down the Hound of Ulster and his son.'

Cuchulainn picked up the shield from the body and his fingers traced the crest. 'There is no one who can give me satisfaction for your death. I would fight a hundred and another hundred...if it was the king himself I would shorten his days.' He was silent for a moment, thinking of all the heroes of the Red Branch. 'It is well it was not one of them, not Conall, nor Forbuide, nor Dubthach the Black Beetle of Ulster.' He touched the dead body again. 'And it was well it was not Cormac nor his armies that gave you this wound. But it is a pity,' he shouted suddenly, 'that it was not an enemy from Munster or Leinster or from the rough country of Cruachu! If I could do vengence on Maeve, or on some king in a far country, in Spain or in Greece, or the land of the Saxons, I would not have this death gnawing at my heart. Have I come to this, to be defeated, to be without strength and comfort and alone? I have no son now to live after me, and no brother to carry on my name. I am a man,' he continued slowly, 'who has killed his own son. I am a man like a raven with no home, or a ship without a rudder on an endless sea. I am a solitary apple left on the tree and the fine green branch has withered under me.'

Conchobor stood a little distance away, watching, with the men of Ireland.

'I think he should be left to his grief,' Cuinaire said and, at that moment, Cuchulainn stood up and faced them.

'If he turns on us,' Conchobor said, troubed, 'by the end

45

of the day he will have killed every man in Ulster.' He beckoned Cathbad the Druid. 'Put an enchantment on him, Cathbad,' the king ordered, 'and have him go down to Baile's Strand and fight the waves for three days.'

Cathbad did as he was bid and Cuchulainn found himself going down towards the sea without any conscious thought of his own. But on the strand he saw a huge white stone and he took his sword and split it. 'That is for Aoife,' he said. 'I would quarter her the same way.'

He fought long and hard with the stones and the waves for three days and three nights until he fell exhausted from hunger and weakness and they came then and took him home to Dundealgan to recover.

Some said he got his death on Baile's Strand but it was not so: he met his death on the plain of Muirthemne.

THE DEATH OF CUCHULAINN

Cuchulainn made his mark on history by winning the great cattle war but he was more than just a great general and a soldier of enormous personal courage. He was a man larger than life; a man who could turn himself into a terrifying monster in battle; a man who was loved and adored by three times fifty queens; a man who, endearingly, could fall in love himself and become as weak as a woman. He was gentle, handsome and implacable, adored by thousands and, inevitably, hated with great venom by hundreds.

He was not allowed to rest for long on the laurels won in the battles at the Ford. His enemies were nursing their wounds and the sons and daughters of the men who Cuchulainn had killed were plotting their revenge. First and foremost was Maeve, who had fled ignominiously back to Connacht when her armies were defeated. Then there were three other formidable enemies with old scores to settle. One was Eric, the son of Cairbre, who Cuchulainn had killed at Rosnaree; another was Lugaid, son of Curoi, who had died at the champion's hand in his own house in Munster and then there were the three daughters of Calatin.

Curoi, years before, had conceded the championship of Ulster to Cuchulainn, no easy thing for any man to do but, what was worse, Blanad, Curoi's wife, met Cuchulainn a little while afterwards and told him that she loved him more than anyone else on earth. If Cuchulainn had a weakness it was his susceptibility to women. When Blanad asked him to bring his men to Curoi's *dún* at Finglas and take her away by force the prospect delighted him. He set out with his men and marched as far as a wood near Curoi's house and then sent word to Blanad that he was waiting.

She immediately returned a message that he was to come for her when the stream in the wood turned white.

Blanad waited until all the men in the *dún* were away looking for stones to build a new house and then she milked the three white red-eared cows which her husband had stolen from her father. She put the milk into a great cauldron that Curoi had brought away at the same time and poured the milk into the stream. Cuchulainn saw the white water and understood the signal. He went straight up to the house but unfortunately he found Curoi there before him. It may have been that he had got word of the group of men in the wood, or perhaps his wife's behaviour made him suspicious. Whatever the reason the two men faced each other and fought. Cuchulainn killed Curoi and brought Blanad away with him.

Curoi was a great lord and much loved. His poet, Feirceirtne, angry and full of pain at his master's death, followed the lovers. He wanted to avenge Curoi but he had no plan of action in his mind. As it happened, he caught up with the pair at Cian Bear and he saw Blanad standing alone on the edge of a high rock. He crept up to her quietly and as she turned suddenly he put his arms around her and threw both of them off the headland to be dashed to pieces on the rocks below. Cuchulainn had to return to Ulster without his prize but Curoi's son still lived and he bided his time.

Calatin's end was different. He was killed in a straightforward battle with Cuchulainn at the Ford but all his twenty-seven sons and his son-in-law were killed with him. He left behind only his wife, who was pregnant. In the course of time she gave birth to triplets, all daughters and each with only one eye.

Maeve heard about the posthumous birth so she came from Cruachu to visit Calatin's wife and offered to take the children away and rear them. They were ugly children and their mother let them go without much hesitation. Maeve mutilated them further by having their right legs and left arms cut off, so that they might be even more odious and horrible and all the more fit for the profession she had planned for them. Calatin, Maeve knew, had been a wizard; his hideous daughters would make ideal candidates to follow in his footsteps and so, when they were old enough, she sent them to the four corners of the world to learn every charm and spell and all the aspects of witchcraft which were known to man and fairy alike. They returned to Maeve, eventually, as tools, polished and honed to perfection in evil, and as dangerous and fatal as Cuchulainn's famous weapon, the Gae-bolga. She had fed their minds from infancy with hatred of Cuchulainn and now they were not only anxious to avenge their father's death, but fully equipped to do so.

On their return Maeve went to greet them on the lawn at Cruachu. She had seen them coming as she sat in her sunny parlour and she had time to put on her most beautifully embroidered cloak — and her legendary charm — before she went outside to sit with them.

'You are fully qualified?' she asked them, after she had disposed of the niceties of conversation and established that their health was good and their journeys had been enjoyable.

'We have learned everything you told us to learn,' they said, 'and we can remember it all. Best of all we now have the power to make the illusion of terrible battles.'

'Nothing will tempt Cuchulainn more,' Maeve said. She invited the awful trio into the house and clapped her hands for the servants to make apartments ready and to bring the finest food and every comfort for the daughters of Calatin. When she saw them comfortably settled she sent for Lugaid and Eric.

'Do you remember,' she asked each of them, 'who killed your father?'

'Cuchulainn,' they said, 'how could either of us forget it?'

'I have three people here who remember it well too,'

Maeve said and told them how she had reared the daughters of Calatin. 'There isn't a king or chief or warrior in the four provinces of Ireland who hasn't lost a son or a brother or a friend or a father in the war for the brown bull or at some other time, by the hand of Cuchulainn. I suggest,' Maeve continued, meaning that she had made up her mind and no one was going to change it for her, 'that we should gather together a great army from Munster, Leinster and Connacht and make a concerted drive on Ulster, because this is the time that their sickness has come upon them.'

Eric and Lugaid agreed, not only because it was politic to do so but because, for once, she was right. They went back to their respective kings in Munster and Leinster and asked them to prepare their armies.

The three forces assembled at Cruachu. Maeve had ordered a feast and the festivities went on for three days and nights. On the fourth day the huge assembled force set out towards Ulster. Maeve had decided not to bring Fergus with them. She knew that however bitter Fergus felt about the slaughter of the sons of Usna, which was why he had left Ulster and become her man and had committed himself to the cause of her country, he would never stand with her against Cuchulainn. The three armies made a start by raiding the borders at Magh Breagh, Midhe and Teathfa. Conchobor, king of Ulster, knew exactly what his enemies had in mind and that Maeve was at the head of the whole business.

'Bring Cuchulainn to Emain where he will be safe,' Conchobor said to his servant, Levarcham, 'until our army is ready to face the three provinces. All we need is time. But tell Cuchulainn that I need him to train the soldiers because he won't come here simply to protect himself. It won't take long for us to get ready. There is scarcely a man in Ulster who doesn't have some grudge to settle with Connacht.'

'Or with Leinster or Munster,' Levarcham added.

Levarcham found Cuchulainn on the strain at Baile. He

was trying to bring down birds with his sling. The birds flew past, cawing and mocking and he couldn't manage one hit. It was a bad omen and he knew it. He had had a heavy heart since Aoife's son had been killed by him in the same place. He felt that time was running out and life had been drunk too deeply and too many had died.

'Conchobor sent me to ask you to help him,' Levercham said to him. She told him about the border raids and that Conchobor had decided to assemble all the strength of Ulster at Emain.

'I would prefer to defend myself here in my own home,' Cuchulainn said.

Levercham gave Loeg, Cuchulainn's charioteer a look.

'It would be best for you to go to Emain,' Loeg said, quickly.

Emer, who had seen Levercham coming and watched the discussion from her window, came out to see what was happening. Loeg and Levercham drew her to one side and advised her to get Cuchulainn to Emain and to keep him there at all costs. So she ordered her chariot and instructed the servants to drive the cattle to Slieve Cullinn in the north and, for the first time in very many years, Dúndealgan was deserted. Cuchulainn left with great reluctance as Dúndealgan was his inheritance and his home. He also had a strong feeling that he would never see it again. Emer, though, left with a great feeling of relief. She knew that it would be much easier to protect Cuchulainn at Emain and that she would have plenty of help in keeping him there.

Conchobor had sent for his druids who advised him to keep the warrior chief in his own brightly-lit crystal house and to send all the poets, story-tellers and the men of science of Emain to entertain him. The druids also told the king to keep Cuchulainn surrounded by beautiful women but this was something Emer did by instinct, always careful to stay near his side herself so that he should not become too distracted. Conchobor warned everyone of the importance of keeping Cuchulainn safe at Emain. 'For if anything

51

happens to him,' he said, 'the whole province of Ulster is at risk. We are as helpless as babes with this accursed sickness.' There was one bad moment when Conchobor went to a feast given by Conall in Cuailgne and didn't invite Cuchulainn to go with him. That was the night when Cuchulainn tried to set fire to the whole settlement of Emain but Scumac, the story-teller, managed to quieten him and succeeded in keeping the hero in the palace.

Maeve and her armies were still robbing and destroying the border lands of Ulster but when she heard that Cuchulainn had been lured to safety she sent for the daughters of Calatin. They listened to her quietly and then smiled and went like the wind to Emain and sat down on the lawn outside Cuchulainn's house. They began to tear up the earth and the grass; made fuzz-balls of stalks and oak leaves; and made sounds like the confused shouts and groans which come in the middle of a battle.

Geanann the druid had been detailed to keep watch on Cuchulainn that day. The sounds of fierce fighting came in through the open windows of the house and Cuchulainn jumped up to see what was happening.

'The town is surrounded,' he said, reaching for his sword.

Geanann hurried over to him and held him back. 'It's witchcraft,' he said, 'there is no battle.'

'Are you telling me,' Cuchulainn asked, struggling to get free from Geanann's grip, 'that I don't know the sound of two armies locked together in mortal combat?'

'It's the daughters of Calatin,' Geanann said, 'setting a trap. Surely you can understand that?'

'I understand only one thing,' Cuchulainn replied, 'and that is that I'm a soldier and there's a battle going on out there and I have to do something about it.'

Geanann called Cathbad and the rest of the wise men of Ulster and they all told Cuchulainn the same thing but it took some time to calm him and hold him back. The next day Cathbad watched Cuchulainn himself. The noises started again outside the window and Cuchulainn rushed over to look. He saw, or thought he saw, the whole army of Ireland on the plain in front of the house. He thought he saw Gradh, son of Lir, standing there and he heard a harp playing enchanted music. He knew that to see and hear these things broke two sacred *geasas* and that his time had come and that all the courage and fine deeds of the world would not save him.

But being Cuchulainn he wanted to fight the wizards and druids that had worked the enchantment. Cathbad did the best he could with him. He told Cuchulainn that if he would stay quietly in Emain for another three days the enchantment would be broken; Conall would be able to come to his help and between them the world would be theirs.

A crow flew past the window, crying and shouting mocking words, 'go out and defend your house and land.' It was one of the one-eyed half-women of Calatin.

Cuchulainn's friends closed in around him. They sang sweet songs to drown the music of the *Sidhe*, told him stories with quiet desperation and did all they could to occupy him until it was time for him to sleep. While he rested Emer and her women and the druids discussed the situation. There was to be no sleep for them. They decided to take him to a lonely glen called Deaf Valley and spent the rest of the night working out the kind of entertainments they would need to keep him there.

'We'll need very little,' Conchobor said when he was consulted, 'because if all the men in Ireland were shouting and fighting and screaming in the vicinity, he'd hear nothing there. It's truly the Valley of the Deaf.'

The next morning the daughters of Calatin were up bright and early searching Emain for Cuchulainn.

'He's gone,' one said, 'hidden by that accursed druid, Cathbad.'

'Emer is still here,' another said.

'But his mistress, Niamh, has gone,' said a third, with a snigger.

'Which gives me an idea,' said the first daughter of Calatin.

They flew over the whole province of Ulster searching for Cuchulainn. He had indeed gone with Niamh and with Emer's blessing, because she knew that of all the women who loved him, he would listen to Niamh above all others.

'Go with Niamh, my darling,' Emer said. 'Little Hound, I never asked you a favour, never in all our life together, but this one. I never stopped you from any adventure, or battle, or deed of valour but, for my sake, my first love, my darling of all the men in the world, go with Cathbad and Ceannann and Niamh and they will make a feast for you.'

Niamh, at a look from Emer, went over to Cuchulainn and gave him three loving kisses and he took her hand and put out the other to Cathbad and agreed to go with them. But when they got to the silent valley Cuchulainn reigned in his horse.

'I have never seen a place that I liked less than this,' he said, 'and the men of Ireland will say that I came to escape my enemies. I have never, never done a cowardly deed. Any man who says so will lose his head on the spot,' he added. Niamh moved closer to him.

'You gave me your word,' she said, 'You promised that you wouldn't go out to meet the men of Ireland without leave from me.'

'If I have never been called a coward,' Cuchulainn said, heavily, 'then I have never broken my word either.'

The horses were set free to graze in the valley. Cuchulainn sighed and went to stroke the manes of Grey of Macha and Black Sainglain. They nuzzled up against him and then he went sadly into the house which Cathbad had prepared. There was, as promised, a great feast with games and drinking and music and laughter. It was all done with the object of distracting Cuchulainn and, as so often happens when people are trying too hard, it showed. Not surprisingly Cuchulainn was restless. Even Niamh's beauty and tender smile could not make him entirely forget why he was there. In the little silences which fell between the songs and the poems he could be seen listening carefully, his head slightly to one side, for the men of Ireland coming to attack Ulster.

The children of Calatin, frustrated by Cuchulainn's disappearance from Emain, summoned an enchanted wind to carry them all over Ulster. They searched every remote forest and glen and every cave and secret path but they couldn't find any sign of him. Eventually they came to the Valley of the Deaf and, although the house was well hidden, they saw Grey of Macha and Black Sainglain grazing on the lawn and Loeg, Cuchulainn's charioteer, standing beside them. They looked at each other triumphantly, and began to make the kind of spells that they had used at Emain.

Thistles and fuzz balls and stalks of oak took on the appearance of battalions of troops. Battle noises, the clash of swords and the screams of the wounded and dying tore the air. In the house the musicians struck up strident airs. The voices of the singers rose and the women laughed louder and more often but it wasn't enough to drown the dreadful sounds outside.

'The whole of Ireland is outside the door and I am eating and drinking and toying with women. My reputation is ruined and Ulster's with it,' Cuchulainn said.

'It is only the children of Calatin,' Cathbad said, 'just as it was at Emain. Take no notice of them, or it really will be the end of you.'

'I wish I could believe you,' Cuchulainn answered, making for the door.

'You can,' Cathbad replied. He pulled Cuchulainn back and the druids made a circle around him and persuaded him to stay inside.

Even wizards get tired of their spells and the noise that the children of Calatin made was too much for their ears, particularly since it seemed to have no effect. Badb, one of the wizard's daughters was extremely tired of it.

'Keep watch,' she told her sisters, 'I'm going to get into the house even if it kills me.'

Badb made her way carefully into a group of servants some distance from Cuchulainn. She took on the appearance of one of Niamh's women and beckoned Niamh to come over to her. Niamh went over, thinking there was some message from Emain, and some of the other women followed her. Badb asked them to come out into the valley with them. She led the group some distance from the house and then used magic to raise a thick mist so that Niamh and the women couldn't find the house again. She herself rose up over the mist and went back to the banqueting hall. This time she put on the appearance of Niamh and went over to Cuchulainn. The sounds of battle were still at full volume around them. Badb smiled, her sisters were doing their work well.

'Dúndealgan has been burned,' she said. 'Muirthemne is destroyed and so is Conaille Muirthemne.'

'What are you saying?' Cuchulainn asked.

'Up! Up!' Badb said. 'The men of Ireland have swept through Ulster and I will be blamed for holding you back.' She knew that Cuchulainn had given his oath to Niamh. 'Conchobor will have me killed on account of it,' Badb continued, 'if I don't let you go and get satisfaction from the men of Ireland.'

Cuchulainn stared at her. 'I thought that you would not let me go for all the riches of the world.'

Badb didn't answer. She knew that her work was done.

Cuchulainn called for his battle clothes. 'If you,' he said, 'are the one to let me go and face all the men of Ireland, then there is no reason for me to stay or any reason to preserve my life.'

As he pinned his cloak together with his gold brooch it fell and pierced his foot.

'That is another broken *geasa*,' Cuchulainn said. 'At least the brooch is a friend who has given me warning, but Niamh,' he shook his head, 'Niamh has let me go.'

The real Niamh eventually found her way through the mist back to the house. She met Cuchulainn at the door in all his battle array. Cathbad was trying to quieten him. The children of Calatin had redoubled their noisy efforts and Cuchulainn thought he saw not only the armies of the men of Ireland and those of Ulster in mortal combat but the city of Emain burning and Emer's sun-filled house razed to the ground and the House of the Red Branch full of fire and smoke.

'Dear son,' Cathbad said, 'if you will stay but one more day, I will break this enchantment, because that is all it is. You have to believe me.'

'I have nothing left to live for,' Cuchulainn replied, 'I am going out to face my enemies and Niamh has given me leave to go.'

Niamh, listening, understood everything. She rushed over to Cuchulainn and caught at his cloak.

'I did not give you leave to go,' she said. 'It must have been the enchantment. You gave me your oath.' Tears streamed down her face. 'Little Hound, I would not let you go for all the gold in the world. Stay with me, Cuchulainn, my darling, my love.'

He shook her off. 'I will never believe a woman again,' he said, and Niamh burst into torrents of sobs and told him about Badb leading her through the valley and the mist and the enchantment but Cuchulainn did not believe her. He could, in any case, hardly understand her for her crying and his pride was at stake.

He has been looking for just such an excuse as this, Loeg said to himself, as he went reluctantly, on Cuchulainn's orders, to yoke the battle chariot. The horses were equally reluctant. Instead of coming over when he shook the bridles Black Sainglain ran away and Grey of Macha would not let Loeg near him at all. Another bad omen, Loeg thought as he went back to Cuchulainn.

'It would take all the men of Ulster to bring Grey of Macha over to me. He knows, what everyone but you knows, that what you are doing is madness. I have never refused you anything,' Loeg went on, 'but if you want the chariot yoked, you will have to come and do it yourself.'

Cuchulainn went on to the lawn and the horse turned his left side three times to the master.

'What is wrong with you?' Cuchulainn demanded, angrily. The horse came up to him and huge round tears of blood fell from Grey of Macha's eyes on to Cuchulainn's feet. 'The chariot has been broken,' Cuchulainn said, 'by one of my so-called friends, so that I can't go into battle, and now you turn on me.' The horse held his head in shame and allowed Cuchulainn to yoke him to another chariot.

Then the women tried to bar his way. Fifty queens stood in the path of the chariot and uncovered their breasts. Such a thing had never happened to a hero of Ulster. Another *geasa* broken, Loeg thought to himself. His master scarcely gave the swelling royal loveliness a glance. He jumped into the chariot and shouted to Loeg to join him. The hundred battle lights were in his eyes and Loeg knew that now nothing would stop him. They drove as though all the demons in Ireland were after them, stopping only at Emain to speak to Emer.

'At least get down from your chariot,' she said, but Cuchulainn shook his head.

'The enemy has gathered at Muirthemne,' he said, 'and I can't stop until I've avenged all the insults heaped upon Ulster. They are raiding our borders and harassing our herdsmen,' he continued, his voice rising.

'But these are all enchantments,' Emer said, 'and ploys of Maeve to draw you out.' Her voice broke suddenly as she saw his obstinate face. Cuchulainn nodded to Loeg to take up the reins. 'I'm not coming back here,' he said, 'until I've taken the war into their own camp,' and Loeg turned the chariot to the south and they left the hundred and fifty queens that loved him crying and striking their hands together because they knew that he would never come back to them again. But Emer turned and went into the house so that no one else would see her grief.

Cuchulainn made one other stop on his journey south. He went to say goodbye to his mother, Dechtire. She came out onto the lawn and gave him a cup of wine. Her face was sad because she knew that he was going to meet the men of Ireland and she felt in her bones that this would be the last time. He took the cup and found that it was full of red blood.

'It's no wonder everyone else forsakes me when even my own mother offers me blood to drink, he said.

She washed the cup and filled it again and once more the wine turned to red blood and then she tried again a third time with the same result.

Cuchulainn threw the cup angrily at a rock and it broke in pieces.

'I did not mean . . . ' Dechtire began.

'It's not your fault,' he said, 'my luck has turned. It's over...' His mouth twisted in a wry smile. 'The golden boy, the hero...it couldn't last forever.'

'You mustn't go into battle feeling like this,' she said. 'Wait until Conall has recovered and he will help you.'

'You are wasting your breath,' Loeg said to her quietly.

'I have never turned back from a battle yet,' Cuchulainn said as he jumped back into the chariot, 'and I'm not going to dishonour my name by waiting for a sick warrior to fight for me. My name,' he continued putting great emphasis on each word, 'is worth more to me than life itself.'

He left her standing beside the broken wine vessel. She shaded her eyes and watched until the chariot was a tiny speck in the distance and then, finally, until it was out of sight.

Cathbad had followed Cuchulainn to Dechtire's house and he continued the journey with him towards Leinster. They came to a ford and saw a young girl. She had yellow hair and was thin with an unhealthy white skin. She was washing and wringing out stained red clothing and crying over the task like an old woman.

'Little Hound,' Cathbad said, 'won't you be warned? It's your clothes she's washing. You are going to your death against Maeve's army.'

'I will not turn back!' Cuchulainn replied. 'I do not care if all the women of the *Sidhe* are washing red clothing for me. There will be plenty of blood but from my spear and my sword.'

'I do not want you to go into this fight,' Cathbad said.

'I am glad to go,' Cuchulainn answered.

'Little Hound,' Cathbad began again, 'it will be your last battle.'

'If you want to help me,' Cuchulainn said, 'stop moaning and following me. However much you delay me the result will be the same. I would rather you went back to look after Emer and Conchobor.' He turned sadly to Loeg, 'how often have we come back so happily to Emain and now we are leaving it and all we love.'

So Cathbad recognised the inevitable and left Cuchulainn at the ford and returned to comfort Emer and the royal household while Loeg and Cuchulainn went on their way. After a while they met three hags on the road. They were the three children of Calatin and they were cooking a poisoned dog on a fire of holly twigs. 'More omens,' Loeg said to himself, as they passed the women. Cuchulainn was forbidden to pass a cooking pot but, since he was also under a *geasa* not to eat his own name and the hags were only offering cooked hound, nothing he did could bring him luck.

'Stay a while, Cuchulainn,' one of the women shouted.

'I will not,' said Cuchulainn.

'If we had something better to offer you, you would stay,' another one said, 'great men who despise the poor deserve no respect.'

'Rein in the horses,' Cuchulainn said.

He went over to the hags and one of them passed him the shoulder blade of the cooked dog with her left hand

and he ate it from his left hand. Then he put the bone down under his left thigh and suddenly all that side of his body was paralysed. He dragged himself back into the chariot and Loeg, muttering under his breath about wizardry and hot-headed men who wouldn't listen to any kind of reason, drove him by Slieve Fuad to Cuchulainn's ancestral plain, Muirthemne. There the men of Ireland were ranged to meet him. Eric saw him coming with his sword flaming in his hand and his golden hair spread around his head and full of fiery lights.

'Make a solid wall of your shields,' Eric said, 'Cuchulainn is here.' They didn't see the weakness in his left side and Cuchulainn himself ignored it as he threw himself into combat. He left as many halves of shields and hands and feet and red bones on the ground as there were grains of sand in the sea or stars in the sky and the plain of Muirthemne was grey with the scattered brains of the men of Ireland.

But Eric had another plan.

'Let pairs of soldiers fight each other on every flank of the army,' he said, 'and put a druid with them, to call Cuchulainn over to separate them and then to demand his spear.'

Neither the soldiers nor the druids looked enthusiastic.

'Cuchulainn's spear won't kill you,' Eric said, impatiently. 'It's prophesied that only a king will die from it.'

Cuchulainn wasn't long in spotting the men who were apparently quarrelling. He went over to separate them, at the druid's bidding, and killed each soldier with a blow to the head.

'You have separated them,' the druid said.

'They wouldn't be so silent,' Cuchulainn replied, 'if you hadn't asked me to interfere.'

'And now I'm asking for your spear,' the druid said.

'I think I have more need of it than you,' Cuchulainn answered. 'Every warrior in Ireland is against me.'

'If you refuse me,' the druid said, 'I'll put a magic curse on you.'

Cuchulainn had heard enough of curses in the last few days and he said so. 'But no one is going to curse me for a refusal,' he shouted, as he reversed his spear and threw it at the druid, killing him and nine more at the same time. Lugaid, son of Curoi, picked up the spear.

'Who is going to die by this?' he asked the children of Calatin, who were watching the battle and biding their time.

'A king,' they said, in chorus.

Lugaid threw the spear and it went clean through Cuchulainn's chariot and mortally wounded Loeg. Cuchulainn drew the spear gently from the gaping wound and Loeg's bowels spilled out and the charioteer groaned once and then whispered, 'Many battles, Cuchulainn...' and then fell dead on the cushions. Cuchulainn closed Loeg's eyes and looked down on him for a moment. Then he caught the reins and shouted his thunder battle cry.

'I'll drive my chariot and fight at the same time!' he shouted, his voice ringing across the plain of Muirthemne.

Then he saw two more men quarrelling and one of them called him to help. Again a druid was standing by when Cuchulainn went to the soldier's assistance and, again, the druid called for Cuchulainn's spear.

'I will put a bad name on you,' the druid said, 'if you don't give it to me.'

'I have already paid what is due to my name today,' Cuchulainn said, but the druid had been well coached by the children of Calatin.

'Then I will put a bad name on Ulster,' the druid continued, and Cuchulainn rose to the bait. The druid was killed by the blunt end of the spear and nine more with him in exactly the same way as the first.

Eric picked up the spear and surveyed the massacre.

'Who will be killed by this spear?' he asked the children of Calatin.

'A king,' they chanted.

'You said that before,' Eric pointed out.

'Didn't it kill the king of the charioteers, Loeg, son of Riangabra?' they said.

Eric hurled the spear at Cuchulainn's chariot and it went through Grey of Macha. Cuchulainn drew out the spear and put his arm across the neck of the dying horse and whispered a farewell in his ear. Then Grey of Macha gathered his last remaining strength and galloped away with half his yoke around his neck to Slieve Fuad, where Cuchulainn had first found him.

The children of Calatin ordered a third pair of soldiers to pretend to fight and again Cuchulainn intervened and a druid demanded his spear.

'I'll put a bad name on you,' the druid said.

'I have already defended my name today and defended it well,' Cuchulainn replied.

The druid caught a look from one of the hags.

'I'll put a bad name on Ulster,' he said.

'I've defended that too,' Cuchulainn answered, 'and twice in the one day is more than enough.'

'Then I'll put a bad name on your kindred,' the druid continued.

'You will not,' Cuchulainn shouted. 'By my honour there is only a little life left to me and I'll do you the kindness of showing you how I'll live it.' He threw the spear and again pierced the druid and those who stood around him.

The druid looked up at him from the ground. 'You do your kindnesses unkindly,' he whispered with his last breath. Lugaid took up the spear and went to find the children of Calatin.

'Who will die by this?' he demanded.

'A king,' they replied.

'You've already told Eric that,' Lugaid said.

'Grey of Macha fell,' they answered, 'and he is the king of all the horses in Ireland.'

'But not the king which I'm going to kill now!' Lugaid said. Then he raised the spear and measuring his distance carefully threw it with all his strength. It went through Cuchulainn's body and out at the other side and Black Sainglain broke away from the chariot and rushed away with half the yoke hanging from his neck. He didn't stop until he had plunged into the lake from which Cuchulainn had taken him in far off Munster. His master was left to die alone on the plain of Muirthemne.

Cuchulainn gathered up his own spilled entrails with great difficulty and staggered to a small lake nearby and drank from it and then washed off his blood and the men of Ireland didn't stop him, because it was his last request. He dragged himself, then, to a stone pillar and leaned upright against it and tied himself to it with his breast belt so that he could face his enemies standing and die on his feet. The hero-light still shone around him and the men of Ireland hung back, still afraid of him.

'Shame on you,' Eric said, 'for not striking off his head the way he struck off my father's.'

Then Grey of Macha galloped back across the plain and, with his last remaining strength, bared his teeth and defended his master. He made three attacks on the men of Ireland and killed fifty with his teeth and thirty with each of his hooves.

A bird came to settle on Cuchulainn's head and they thought that he was dead. Lugaid came and grasped Cuchulainn's hair and struck his head from his shoulders as the soldiers gave three great shouts. As Cuchulainn's head was shown to the crowd his sword fell from his hand, cutting off Lugaid's hand, and so they cut off Cuchulainn's hand in revenge. Then the hero-light faded around Cuchulainn's head and the men of Ireland knew that he was indeed dead.

The men of Ireland suggested that Maeve should bring the head to Cruachu, since she had gathered the army together.

'Let Lugaid take it,' Maeve said, 'since he struck it off,' and so Lugaid and his men took the head and went south towards the Liffe river.

Ulster was getting ready to attack her enemies. Conall went ahead of the army and met Grey of Macha with blood draining from him and he knew then that Cuchulainn was dead. He went with the horse to find the body and when they got to the stone pillar Grey of Macha laid his head on Cuchulainn's breast. Conall stroked the dying, heart-broken horse and then went after the army to revenge his friend's death. They had had a pact that whichever of them was killed first the other would get satisfaction for it.

'If I am the first to die?' Cuchulainn had asked, 'how long will you be before you avenge me?'

'Before the evening of the same day,' Conall had promised. 'And you?'

'Before your blood is cold on the ground,' Cuchulainn had replied.

So Conall pursued Lugaid to the Liffe. He found him, guarded by his charioteer, bathing in the river.

'There's a man coming,' the charioteer called, 'and you'd think all the ravens in Ireland were over his head he's moving at such a rate. There's a snow storm ahead of him,' he added.

'He's not coming in friendship then,' Lugaid said, scrambling out of the water. He shaded his eyes to see the horseman more clearly. 'Those aren't ravens, they're the sods of earth flying behind his horses' hooves and the snow is the froth from his mouth.' He paused, watching. 'He's going after the army by the ford. Let him pass by. I've no mind to fight with him.'

But Conall had seen them and reined in his horse.

'It's good to meet a debtor,' Conall said to Lugaid, 'Cuchulainn is dead and I am here now to collect payment.'

Lugaid could not refuse the challenge. He agreed to fight it out on the plain of Magh Argetnas and Conall succeeded in wounding Lugaid with his spear. Later they moved the fight to Ferta Lugdac.

'Fair play?' Lugaid asked wearily.

'What fair play?' Conall asked, still full of battle anger.

'I have only one hand,' Lugaid said, 'bind one of yours to your side.'

'Very well,' Conall replied. They fought like that for a long time without either getting the better of the other. Then Conall's horse, Dub-dearg, came up to Lugaid and took a bite out of his side.

'That was not fair,' Lugaid gasped, as he fell.

'I only promised fair play for myself,' Conall said. 'How could I promise it from a dumb animal? We are all sworn to avenge Cuchulainn.'

Lugaid closed his eyes. 'Don't prolong it,' he asked, 'take my head and put it with Cuchulainn's and my kingdom alongside his and my courage with your courage. I give you the championship of Ireland.'

Conall was moved and made a quick end to him but he could not find Cuchulainn's head among those who had fallen. So he put together as many heads as he could, in a row on a withy-wand thrust through their mouths from cheek to cheek, and went back to Emain with the news.

He found Emer sitting in her upper room, looking out over the plain and waiting for some word from the battle. When they heard what had happened the whole countryside was filled with the sounds of crying and weeping. There were burning tears and sharp cries and Emer, distraught, gathered her women and they went to the place where Cuchulainn's body was and they gave themselves up to their grief.

'There never fell a better hero than Cuchulainn; he had courage all his life, even as a soft child. Until all the chiefs of Ireland have fallen by my hand, there will be no peace,' Conall said. 'He should not have gone into battle without me at his side and there will be no laughter or happiness now that the Hound has left us.' He fell silent for a moment, looking at the mutilated body then, in a low voice, he continued, 'they couldn't have done it without the spells of the accursed children of Calatin.'

Conall left the keening women and drove his way through Ireland, leaving a trail of blood and desolation behind him. He killed Eric first at Teamhair and hundreds with him. Eric's sister, Acaill, came to find the grave and wept over it for nine days until her heart broke like a nut inside her and she was buried as she had asked, in a place where Eric's mound and grave could be seen and, afterwards, the place was called Acaill. Then Conall killed the children of Calatin and finally he found what he had been looking for, the head of Cuchulainn, which was being used as a football by two men near Tara.

'If this was Eric's land, I would burn the pillage and raze everything to the ground but since it is the very heart and meeting place of Ireland, I will spare Tara,' Conall said.

He brought back the head to Emer and her joy at seeing it was equal only to her grief at his death. She took it and washed it clean and wrapped a silk cloth around it and pressed it to her breast and began to cry and to suck the blood from it.

'This head was so beautiful,' she said, 'and all the kings and the princes of the world would weep to see it the way it is now. I remember every moment of our life together. There was not one woman who did not envy me for the goods and jewels you brought me, but without the wealth and the tributes and the rents from the whole world, they would still have envied me for you were a man as no other man.' Her voice broke completely, and she wept bitterly and then she held the head away from her and gazed into the dead face. 'It is thirty days since we lay together,' she continued, 'and thirty since I saw your bright eyes and kissed your sweet mouth and heard your voice and saw the love in your face. I am glad,' she continued, her voice strong again, 'that I never brought shame on you because I loved you always and was faithful to my love.' Emer unpinned her hair and let it fall loose about her shoulders

67

for the last time. 'We were so happy together, my love,' she whispered to Cuchulainn's dead mouth, 'and if the world was searched from end to end from the rising of the sun to the waning of the moon, the likes of us would never have been found in the one place again. You and me and Loeg and Black Sainglain and the Grey of Macha...Ulster has lost its strength and beauty now.'

Then Emer made a circle of the lawn and gazed at the heads of heroes, which Conall had brought back from Muirthemne and said to him, 'tell me about them again.'

'Sweet Emer, it is in revenge for the Hound that I brought these heads,' he said. 'That with the black hair and the red cheek smoother than a rose is Eric, son of Cairbre.'

They toured the heads together and marvelled that they had not changed colour while they lay on the grass.

'That one,' Conall said, 'with soft hair and eyes like ice is a son of Maeve.'

'He is more beautiful than any of the others,' Emer remarked.

'He was a destroyer,' Conall said.

'And that one, to the west, with grief still on his face?' Emer asked.

'That is Lugaid, who killed the Hound,' Conall said simply.

'And those three dark ones to the north, with blue faces so evil that even you turn from them?'

'They are the daughters of Calatin; they are the ones Maeve brought up with spells and enchantment; they are the ones who truly killed the Hound.'

Emer turned away in disgust. 'One-eyed witches,' she exclaimed, under her breath. 'Why didn't he listen to me?'

'That is the king of Leinster of the Speckled Swords,' Conall went on, 'and those the brave Culainn and hardy Cunlaid, that I left in a pool of their own red blood.'

'Enough,' Emer said, 'ten and seven scores of hundreds have fallen in revenge for the head of Cuchulainn. Does everyone mourn the Hound as we do?' Emer asked.

'I do not know how we are to live without him,' Conall said.

'It's finished,' Emer answered. 'I have no more vengeance in me.'

She told Conall to make a wide deep grave for Cuchulainn and then she lay down beside her dead husband and put her mouth to his mouth.

'Love of my life, my friend, my sweetheart, my one man in the whole world,' she said, 'I have no wish to live without you,' and then her soul left her body and Conall laid them both in the one tomb and raised a stone over it and wrote their names in Ogham on it. Afterwards he led the funeral rites himself, and all the men of Ulster mourned their dead hero, but the three times fifty queens that loved him swore that they saw him appear in a druid chariot going across the lawn at Emain and that they could hear him singing the music of the *Sidhe*.

FERGUS AND THE MONSTER

When Fergus Mac Léide was king of Ulster there was a minor civil war in the midlands of the country in which the celebrated Conn of the Hundred Battles was victorious. His rival, Eochu, fled to Ulster in fear of his life but later returned to his own lands under King Fergus's protection. On the way home Eochu was set upon by Conn's men and murdered. Fergus, furious and deeply insulted that someone under his protection had been killed, rushed into battle with such ferocity that Conn quickly sued for peace and made recompense with tracts of land south of the Boinne. In addition the Princess Dorn, daughter of a minor king in Conn's territory, gave herself up to Fergus in place of her son, who had been one of Eochu's assassins. She lived in the palace as one of the Ulster king's personal women. Outwardly she was pleasant but inwardly she nursed her grievances and bided her time.

After that peace reigned for a while in Ireland. Ulster was strong and the other Irish kings knew it. So they managed to reign side by side with only minor skirmishes on their borders. Only one king seemed unaware of the strength of Fergus and that was Iubhdán, king of the Lupracans, the tiny water sprites who lived beneath the sea.

One day, as a great banquet was being prepared at Emain Macha for Fergus and the men of Ulster, a similar feast was beginning in Lupra under the sea. At Lupran feasts, as in mortal ones, the entertainment was provided by musicians and poets and by feats of strength and endurance by the most famous champions. In Lupra there was a man who could fell a thistle with a single blow. It usually took twelve men to hack through the stem, so small were the men of

70

Lupra. At these Lupran feasts there were also great vats of old ale, mountains of meat, hundreds of servants, noise and laughter and, of course, boasting. In other words, apart from the scale of things, one royal banquet proved to be much like any other.

At Iubhdán's high table sat his wife, Bébhó, his heir, Beg, his poet Esirt, Glomar the strong man and many others. The king was in a convivial mood. He raised his drinking horn.

'To Lupra!' he said, and they all cheered, 'and my people.'

Those nearest to him stood up to pay him homage and Iubhdán bowed his head graciously.

'Have you ever seen a king better than myself?' he asked, taking a deep drink out of the horn.

'We have not!' they said.

'Or a strong man any better than my strong man?' he asked.

'We have not,' they said again.

'Or better warriors or horses than we have at our court tonight?'

'Never!' they shouted.

'On my oath,' Iubhdán said, completely carried away by the drink and the cheers of his men and the high excitement of the occasion, 'I wager no one could attack us and take a single captive tonight, we have such strength and so many heroes. Anyone of you,' he said, waving his drinking horn and spilling a fair amount of ale, 'anyone of you, nay, each one of you, are the stuff of which kings are made.'

At which Iubhdán sat down abruptly and his poet Esirt burst out laughing.

'And what is the joke?' the king asked coldly.

'I know of a country not far from here where one man could lift up four of our battalions single-handed.'

'Treason!' Iubhdán shouted, 'take him!' and two soldiers rushed forward and grabbed the poet by the arms.

'You'll regret this,' Esirt said, 'by arresting me you have

71

started a terrible series of events. You will be the prisoner, not me and not here, but in Emain Macha and you won't escape without leaving behind your most precious possession.'

'I don't believe that,' the king said, but he hesitated before ordering Esirt to the dungeons.

'There is a great feast this very night in Ulster as happy and as full of drink and music as this one, but great evil will come out of it. I will go there . . ' Esirt went on, as Iubhdán opened his mouth to speak, ' . . . and I will float in King Fergus's goblet until I almost drown and . . . '

'What makes you think you are going anywhere?' the king asked.

'Because if you give me three days to go to Emain Macha I will bring something back to prove that what I say is true. If I don't find any such token then you may do what you like with me.'

'Oh very well,' Iubhdán said as there didn't seem much point in disagreeing; his feast was ruined beyond redemption so he may as well find out what Esirt was talking about. 'Go to Emain Macha if you must. Set him free,' he told the guards.

Esirt bowed his way out and went to his quarters and prepared himself for the Ulster court. He put on a smooth silk shirt and his gold-embroidered tunic and scarlet cloak, which was fringed with pale gold. On his feet he wore tiny white bronze shoes, again decorated with gold, and he carried the white bronze wand of a poet. Over his head he pulled a silken hood and he drew himself up to his full miniscule height and set out by the easiest road to Ulster. At the gates of Emain Macha he shook his poet's rod and the gate-keeper came out to see who was there. At first he didn't see Esirt. The Lupra poet was thigh-high in the close-cropped grass of the lawns but, after a while, a gleam of gold caught the servant's eye. He stared at the tiny creature and then bent down to speak to him, nearly blowing Esirt over with the strength of his breath. A few moments later the gate-keeper went to report to Fergus, who was surrounded by his chiefs.

'Is he smaller than Aedh?' Fergus asked, amused. Aedh, the Ulster poet, was a dwarf, who could stand comfortably on the hand of an ordinary-sized man.

'This creature could stand on Aedh's palm!' the gate-keeper said and the court burst out laughing.

'Send him in, I can't wait to see him,' one of the ladies said and Fergus nodded his permission to the gate-keeper.

'I'm curious myself,' he said.

Esirt was almost smothered by the attention he got on all sides. Everyone wanted to talk to him and to pick him up and examine his elegant clothes. He put out his hands in protest.

'You're all huge,' he complained, 'and I'm sure your breath is infected. Give me some room to breathe.'

'Yes, leave him be,' Fergus said. He smothered a smile. 'He is a guest, after all.'

The men of Ulster moved back and Esirt looked around. 'Let him be my companion,' he said, eventually, pointing to the dwarf. 'He would be a giant in my country, but he is the smallest here.'

Aedh bent down and placed Esirt on his palm and then lifted him up so that he could see and be seen in safety.

'Well,' Fergus said, 'Tell me about yourself.'

'I am Esirt the chief poet of Lupra,' the little man said, drawing himself up to full height.

'The court poet?' Fergus asked.

'Exactly,' Esirt replied.

'Then you must drink and eat with us,' Fergus said.

'I will neither eat nor drink with you,' Esirt said, coldly.

'In that case,' Fergus said, bored, 'put him in the cup and he can soak up wine whether he likes it or not.'

The cup-bearer dropped Esirt into the cup and he floated round and round in the wine, yelling furiously.

'I've come here to give your poets my knowledge and all you can do is try to drown me!'

73

'Better fish him out,' Fergus said. He smothered a yawn. Simple amusements do not distract royals for very long. A soft satin napkin was produced and Esirt was lifted out of the cup and dried off carefully.

'Perhaps you could tell us why you won't eat our food?' Fergus said, when the little man was set before him again.

'It is a question of your court,' Esirt said. He hesitated. 'But I do not wish to displease the king,' he added slyly.

'Make your judgement,' Fergus said. 'I give you my word I will not be displeased.'

'You yourself, I gather,' Esirt said, 'trifle with your steward's wife while your foster-son ogles the queen.'

'Go on,' said Fergus, coldly, and the captive Princess Dorn, who was under the impression that she alone enjoyed the king's favour, looked equally annoyed.

'There are fair accomplished women here. You should not let them to the mercy of...' Esirt looked around at the rather rough warrior-heroes, '...these mere chieftains, when there is a king of your stature in the land.'

Fergus thawed slightly. 'You are probably right,' he said. He did not look at the Princess Dorn. 'A man of veracity,' he added dryly.

'And you are not angry?'

'I acknowledge my interest in my steward's wife. Presumably you are right about the rest,' Fergus said, and the Princess Dorn stalked out of the room

'Then since you admit the evil, I will sit down and eat with you,' Esirt said. Lack of courage was not one of his faults. He made himself comfortable on the table and Fergus started to smile. He waved his hand for food to be given to the Lupracan.

'Would you like to hear about Lupra?' Esirt asked, between mouthfuls.

'If they are all like you,' Fergus said, 'we would indeed.'

'King Iubhdán is a handsome, well-loved king. His voice is sweet; his hair is black as night and his colour like that of the rowan-berry and the river's foam. He is strong and well-formed and his eyes are clear and bright and he heads a great army in all its golden-haired glory.'

'I see,' Fergus said, 'and how big is he?'

'Oh, he is tall and proud and imperious.'

'Taller than you?' Fergus asked.

'A little,' Esirt admitted.

'As tall as me?' Fergus queried.

'No,' Esirt said, shortly. He went on quickly, before there were any more unwelcome interruptions. 'My king loves the hunt and he has a squadron of grand bridled horses. All the warriors of Lupra have golden hair, save our king, and all the women are beautiful. There is fine music, deep and melodious from silver horns and there is great feasting and grandeur and merriment at the court. Much as women love you, King Fergus of Ulster,' Esirt said, throwing on one side some salmon bones, 'it is completely surpassed by the desire they feel for Iubhdán.'

The men of Ulster settled themselves back on their couches and prepared to enjoy themselves. There hadn't been quite so much fun at a banquet in Ireland for a long time. The feast went on for the customary three days and nights and, at the end of it, when Esirt was preparing to leave, Fergus and the Ulster chiefs tried to give him gifts of gold and treasure. Indeed they had all enjoyed themselves so much that the pile of gifts for their entertaining guest reached the height of the tallest of the Ulster warriors.

'I don't want your gifts,' Esirt said, loftily. 'In my country every man has sufficent and more than he needs.' He was, the Ulster men realised, going to be awkward to the last.

'We can't take back what we've given,' they said, 'it wouldn't be right. Not even if we had given you our wives and cattle.'

'Then divide it between you,' Esirt said, passing his poet's judgement, 'two thirds to yourselves and one third to your stableboys and jesters.'

'May I go with you?' Aedh asked, 'I would like to see

75

your country.'

'Please yourself,' Esirt said, in an off hand way, although, in fact, it suited him very well. 'I won't say that you will be welcome and then when you find that my people treat you well, you will be all the more grateful.'

So they set out, the dwarf, who was a giant at the side of the other, and the tiny, neat little man from Lupra. They were both dressed in their finery and carried their poets' wands. In spite of Esirt's short legs, he was able to keep up with, indeed pass, Aedh on the road.

Iubhdán sent his magical water horse to carry them over the sea. The Lupracans had control over water and the horse was a very strange animal. He had a crimson mane and green legs and a long tail which lay on the water in curls. His bridle was of gold and his eyes flashed fiery red. Aedh was rather reluctant to mount the beast but Esirt persuaded him. They passed quickly and safely over and through the sea to the land of Lupra where Iubhdán and the court were waiting to greet them.

Iubhdán embraced Esirt. 'Welcome back,' he said, but he looked at Aedh warily. 'Why did you bring this giant to destroy us?' he whispered to his poet.

'He is not a giant but a dwarf and a man of science and a poet,' Esirt bowed low before his king, but his eyes were gleaming with triumph. 'I told you I would bring you some proof of the might of Ulster,' he said.

The Lupracans fell back, alarmed, at the sight of Aedh but called out from a safe distance, 'What is the giant's name?'

'The poet Aedh,' Esirt said. He turned to the king. 'Do you accept that what I said was true?' he asked.

'I have to accept it,' the king answered, 'if this man is called a dwarf in his own country.'

'Then you are under my bond,' Esirt said, 'to go to Ulster in the same way that you sent me. And I lay this charge on you — that you be the first to taste the porridge being made tonight for Fergus.'

Iubhdán sighed. He knew when he was beaten. 'Very well,' he said. He went sadly to take leave of his wife, Bébhó.

'I will come with you,' she said, immediately and then added, wife-like, 'but it is all your own fault. You should not have arrested Esirt in the first place.'

'That may be,' Iubhdán answered, 'but I cannot break my word or I will lose my honour.'

The water-horse was again saddled and it bore the king and queen safely across and under the sea to the outskirts of Emain Macha and the two small people found no difficulty in getting into the royal palace.

Nor was it difficult to find the cauldron of porridge. The trouble was to get up the side of it.

'Get the horse,' Bébhó said, with a woman's practical commonsense and, with the animal's help, Iubhdán managed to reach the rim of the cauldron.

'I still can't reach the ladle,' he called down.

'Be careful,' Bébhó said, but it was too late. He stretched too far and slipped and found himself at the bottom of the pot and up to his waist in porridge and there he was held as fast as if there were iron chains around him.

'Get the horse,' he shouted, 'and send to Lupra for help — and gold for a ransom,' he added, 'for they'll be sure to keep me here as long as they can.'

'I can't leave you,' Bébhó said.

'You're a foolish woman if you don't,' he said, irritably.

'Can't you climb out?' she asked.

'This stuff is like glue!' Iubhdán said.

'You should never have tormented Esirt in the first place,' Bébhó said, 'I told you so last night.'

'Would you please go and get help,' the king of Lupra roared, gritting his teeth. 'We can discuss the whys and wherefores at some other time!'

'I'm going to stay here until I see how things go for you,' she said, obstinately and Iubhdán groaned and made another futile attempt to extract his leg from the porridge.

The people of Ulster weren't long in finding the Lupra king in their porridge. They roared with laughter as they watched him try to escape, which did not improve Iubhdán's temper. Eventually they took pity on him and picked him out and carried him to Fergus.

'Another of them,' Fergus said, 'and black-haired, not like the other. You'd better tell us your name, mannikin.'

'I am Iubhdán, king of Lupra,' said the little man, 'and this is my wife and queen. Bébhó is her name.'

'King, eh?' Fergus said as he made a face. 'There seem to be an awful lot of you under my feet at the moment.'

'I am the king,' Iubhdán said, indignantly. 'I have never told a lie in my life. On my honour...'

'Enough,' Fergus said, waving him away. 'Put these creatures with the household servants.'

'Mighty Fergus,' Iubhdán asked, 'please show me some little favour. I cannot stand the foul breath of these common folk. I give you my word that I will stay in Ulster if you will only treat me like an honourable prisoner.'

'I may take your word?' Fergus asked.

'I have never broken it,' Iubhdán answered.

'Very well, then, give him the east chamber,' Fergus said, 'and a servant to tend to his needs.'

Iubhdán was delighted with his accommodation and he stayed in Ulster as he had promised, moving about the country freely and entertaining the people with accounts of Lupra under the sea and his shrewd observances on the lives of the men of Ulster.

'I have a room with a ceiling of red-gold, and a silver floor, in my own palace,' he told the servant who was lighting the fire in his apartment in Emain. 'The hearth is of bronze and copper and the candlesticks are of gold and...' he broke off and frowned as the servant threw a log on to the fire. 'There is woodbine around that,' he said, sharply, 'you should never burn it. Terrible things will happen, drownings, stabbings, dreadful misfortunes. And spare the apple and the willow —'

'What can I burn?' the servant asked, bewildered.

'Rowan, the wizard's tree, and the spiteful briar, but be careful with alder, it's a witch wood. The best thing to burn is holly, green or dry. You will have luck with birch too — that will bring good fortune.'

'This is what they say in Lupra?' asked the servant.

'It is a fact,' Iubhdán replied.

'It must be a strange country,' the man said.

'Not so strange as this,' Iubhdán said. He started to laugh. 'I met a soldier yesterday who was worried that the soles of his shoes were too thin but I told him they would last him all his life.'

'How could you know that?'

'I knew that he would be dead in a fight before the night was out,' the king of Lupra said, 'and he was. In Lupra we do not fight, no one grows old, everyone is happy...' he hesitated and sighed, 'that is except myself and my queen at the present time. No one is ever refused hospitality...' he broke off and stared into the curling flames of the fire and the servant crept away, not wanting to disturb the little man's memories.

After some time the people of Lupra assembled seven battalions and came to Emain to search for their king. Fergus came out to meet them on the lawns. The Lupra soldiers formed neat, well-ordered ranks but they were far too small to be impressive.

'What do you want?' Fergus asked.

'Iubhdán,' they said. 'We will pay you a good ransom.'

Fergus conferred with his chiefs and then came back to the delegation.

'What ransom?' he asked.

'We will cover this vast plain with corn every year without ploughing and without sowing.'

Fergus shrugged. 'I prefer to keep Iubhdán,' he said.

'Then we will have our revenge,' the Lupra men answered.

'What revenge?' Fergus asked.

'We'll let all the calves in to suckle the cows and there won't be one drop of milk in the whole of Ulster.'

'But I'll still have Iubhdán,' Fergus said, turning on his heel.

The Lupracans did exactly as they had threatened and then returned to Emain the following day and offered to undo the damage if Fergus would release their king.

'Iubhdán stays here,' Fergus said.

'Then we will pollute all your water, every well and every river in the province,' said the spokesman for Lupra.

'That won't worry me,' Fergus said.

The next day, having dirtied all the drinking water in the country the seven battalions assembled again on the lawns at Emain and demanded Iubhdán.

'You can't have him,' Fergus said.

'Then we'll burn all the barns and kilns,' shouted the Lupracans.

'As you wish,' Fergus said, 'but you will not get Iubhdán.'

On the fourth day the Lupra men threatened to snip off all the ears of corn in Ulster and they were again refused the king.

'Since we have no barns to put it in, you may as well,' Fergus said.

The Lupracans returned on the fifth day, having spoiled the harvest, and demanded Iubhdán again.

'I will not give him up,' said Fergus.

'Then we will shave the hair off every man and woman in Ulster and they'll be shamed forever!' the Lupracans said, losing patience.

'By my word, I'll kill Iubhdán if you do!' Fergus shouted, and the men of Ulster reached for their weapons.

'Let me speak to them,' Iubhdán said to Fergus. 'I can calm them and get them to repair the mischief they've done.'

'Very well,' said Fergus, 'but do it quickly, or I won't be

responsible for my men.'

Iubhdán was brought out to the front of the crowd and his people cheered, sure that he was going to be released. He held up his hand for silence.

'I am under bond by Esirt,' he said, 'to stay here in Ulster. There is nothing any of us can do, and I ask you now to make good what you have spoiled.'

The Lupracans looked very dejected and muttered among themselves for a moment. Then one man stepped forward.

'All right,' he said. 'We'll make things right, but not for love of you, Fergus of Ulster, only for our king whom you hold prisoner. It is an evil thing, Fergus' he went on, his voice rising, 'to keep Iubhdán...'

Iubhdán held up his hand again. 'Go,' he said. 'Esirt has said that I cannot leave until I give up my most precious possession.' The sight of all his people had made Iubhdán very homesick. He turned to Fergus. 'Will you take my spear? It is a match for a hundred others.'

Fergus shook his head.

'Or my shield,' Iubhdán said, hopefully. 'None will ever be wounded behind it.'

Fergus shook his head again.

'My sword,' the king of Lupra said, suddenly. 'There is no match for it in any royal hand in Ireland. Or my cloak and mantle which will last forever?'

'I do not want these things,' Fergus said.

'My belt of silver and gold, which will keep you from all sickness?'

'No,' said Fergus.

'Or my helmet which will prevent you from baldness.'

Fergus ran his hand through his thick hair. 'No,' he said.

'I have a magic cauldron which will turn stones into meat, or my horse-rod...'

'Horse-rod?' Fergus said, puzzled.

'With this yellow rod in your hand every woman in the world will look at you and give you their hottest love.'

'Mmm,' said Fergus.

'Or my sweet-stringed timpan to delight the women of the universe, or the shears that Barran the smith made. With these shears every man will get a sweetheart.'

'You didn't tell me you had all these treasures,' Fergus said.

'Of all these the finest are my shoes. With those you can travel under and over the seas and all the lands of the world.'

Fergus was still thinking about Iubhdán's magic possessions when Aedh the poet returned from his visit to Lupra, and the tales he had to tell put the matter of Iubhdán's ransom in the background for the while.

'There's a fairy palace of marble, doors of gold, pillars of crystal, columns of silver...silk and satin of every colour on the beds, beautiful woman frolicking in the w...waters of the l...loch...' Aedh was stammering in his excitement. 'Music,' he continued, 'and white-skinned women like swans in my bosom, tiny gentle creatures with golden hair to their toes. And another one...w...would be nestling in my beard,' the Ulster dwarf went on. 'Three hundred women serve the queen and there is no gossip or malice. They wear satin and chains of gold...'

'I have decided,' Fergus said, suddenly. 'I will take your shoes, Iubhdán, so that I can travel under the water like a Lupracan and perhaps even visit your country.'

'I may return to my people?' Iubhdán asked.

'With my good wishes,' Fergus said.

They parted on good terms but, before he left, the king of Lupra warned Fergus that although he may go wherever he wished with the shoes, there was one place that was forbidden and that was Loch Rudraige, not far from the palace at Emain Macha.

'If you go into that lake, I cannot be responsible for the consequences,' Iubhdán said, gravely.

'I won't forget,' Fergus said. He embraced the tiny king and the Ulster people watched sadly as their little guest left at the head of his minature army.

Fergus was delighted with the magic shoes. He explored rivers and lakes and walked under the sea, straight into the water from the strand, as though he was a fish as well as a man. He planned to go to Lupra very soon to sample the delights Aedh had described but, in the meantime, he enjoyed using the shoes in his own territory.

However human nature is human nature and it wasn't long before Fergus was drawn irresistibly to the shores of Loch Rudraige. He stood in his chariot and looked at the dark water and then suddenly ordered his charioteer to drive him straight into the loch. He swam for some time under the water but found it clouded and muddy. Usually he delighted in watching the fishes dart to and fro and in imitating them but today he could see nothing but whirling sand. Then, without warning, a ferocious monster reared up in the water in front of him. It blew itself out to an enormous size and shook itself so much that the water arched up to the height of a rainbow and then fell in a deluge, flooding the hills at the edge of the loch. Fergus, terrified, turned and swam as fast as he could to the shore. The monster drew itself in like a blacksmith's bellows and swam after the king, rapidly overtaking him. When Fergus was almost safe the monster let out his foul breath over the king and Fergus's face was drawn into a hideous rictus, which dragged his mouth halfway round to his ear, making him squint-eyed and distorted. Shaking with fear, Fergus just managed to get to the shore and he dragged himself out and lay panting on the bank.

His charioteer looked at him, horrified.

'What is it?' Fergus asked, when he had got back his breath. 'Do I look badly?'

'No...no...' the charioteer replied. 'You had a lucky escape.' He did not meet the king's twisted eye. 'There's nothing wrong with you that a good night's sleep won't cure.'

He helped his master to the chariot and Fergus fell into a

deep sleep on the cushions and they drove back as quickly as they could to Emain Macha. Before Fergus woke the charioteer went to find the Ulster chiefs to tell them what had happened.

'This is very serious,' they said. 'A disfigured man cannot sit on the throne of Ulster.'

'But this is our own beloved Fergus,' another said. 'We can't just throw him out.'

The elders conferred together for a while, then came back to the charioteer.

'Does he know?' they asked.

'No,' the charioteer said. 'I told him he was all right. He's asleep now.'

'If he finds out he will feel obliged to abdicate,' the most respected of the chiefs said.

'Can it be kept from him?' someone asked.

'It won't be easy,' the elder statesman said, 'but we will try.'

They had another discussion and it was decided to clear the palace of all low-born servants and to have only a very carefully chosen few to look after the king's personal needs. Mirrors were to be removed and care taken that the king did not see his reflection in the water.

'He can lean back to have his head washed,' someone suggested.

'But won't he feel some change in his face himself?' one of the chiefs asked.

'Not if he doesn't wish to believe it,' the elder said, wisely. 'We all hide things from ourselves.'

It can only have been this natural vanity which kept Fergus in happy ignorance of his condition for seven long years, because he was not a stupid man. The chiefs did their work well and Fergus continued to rule with his customary wisdom and strength, shielded from the populace or anyone who might let the secret out. The Ulster elders made one mistake, however. They did not get rid of the Princess Dorn and she continued to take her turn with the other high-born ladies of the court in attending to the king's ablutions.

One day she was very slow in getting the bath water ready and Fergus became irritated. They had an argument about the bath-stone and then a few minutes later she pulled his hair as she was dressing it. Fergus lost his temper and hit her so hard that he broke a tooth and, in retaliation, and also no doubt in return for years of humiliation, she dragged his head around so that he could see himself in the water.

'You'd be better fighting the monster that pulled your mouth half-way round your poll,' she said, 'than hitting helpless women.' Then she rushed away to get a mirror so that there could be no mistake in his mind as to how he really looked. Fergus stared at his own ugly, hardly human reflection in the mirror and then at Dorn's mocking face behind it and he was so overcome with fury that he grabbed his sword and cut her in two on the spot.

'Get me my chariot!' he yelled, in a voice that could be heard all over the palace and out on to the lawns as well. He buckled on his arms and strode like a devil to his chariot.

'Take me to Loch Rudraige,' he said.

'Sire,' the charioteer began and then ducked as Fergus's whip whistled around his ears.

'Without answering me back!' Fergus shouted.

The chariot set off with a swirl of dust behind it. The warriors and heroes hurriedly went for their own horses and chariots and followed the king to the shores of the loch. They found that he had plunged straight into the water. He was wearing Iubhdán's shoes and he stood on top of the waves for a moment and shouted back at the assembled crowd.

'I will have to kill him to cure myself of this disfigurement,' he said. 'I don't want anyone coming in after me.'

The monster was waiting. It was even more terrifying than Fergus remembered. It was three times fifty feet in height with glittering tusks and eyes blazing like torches and three times fifty sharp claw-like flippers on either side of its body.

They fought so furiously in the middle of the loch that the water seethed like a cauldron and salmon leaped on to the shore for safety. Fergus struck at the almost impregnable body of the monster with his sword, over and over again, until he drove it back across the loch. But he was wounded a hundred times himself and the pale water turned crimson with blood. Finally he had the beast trapped near the shore and he hacked it to pieces with his famous sword and cut out the heart and dragged it to the shore and himself with it.

'I am the survivor,' he shouted with his last strength to the men of Ulster and then he fell back dead into the deep waters, his body as full of wounds as a sieve. The men of Ulster, sick at heart, lifted him out. They gathered round the body and Aedh gasped in amazement.

'His face is whole again,' he said. 'He conquered his fear.'

'Was it fear that twisted his mouth?' someone asked.

'And curiousity which brought him here,' Aedh said. He bent down and took off the magic shoes and threw them into the loch, 'and a foolish woman's stupid words.'

FIONN AND THE GILLA DACKER

The Fianna spent their summers hunting; they also put down minor enemies, prevented robberies and exacted fines. From November to May they were quartered on chiefs and landowners in different parts of the country. They received some pay and in return they were expected to defend the country from foreign invaders.

At the beginning of one particular summer Fionn held a council meeting and decided on Munster for the first chase of the season. The hunt was well organised and a huge band of men spread and scattered themselves over every valley plain and wood from Kilkenny down through east Munster and across as far as the Shannon. They made camp after a while on a hill overlooking the great plain to the south of Slievenamon. They were all there: Fionn, Goll and Diarmuid of the Love Spot, Kylta Mac Ronán, Conál Maol of the Foul Tongue, Oscar, Oisín, Fergus the Poet and many others. The hounds were unleashed and Fionn and his friends rested and listened to the noise of the hunt; it was sweet music to Fionn's ears. He loved the baying of the dogs and the shouts of his young warriors and the whistles and signals of the huntsmen. But he didn't relax completely until he had sent Mac Bresal to keep a look-out on the highest point of the hill.

'The Dé Dananns never miss an opportunity,' he said, 'and their druids know we're out hunting.'

Mac Bresal nodded and took up a position where he could see every part of the plain. Fionn asked Oscar to get out the chess-board and they settled down to a game.

A short time later Mac Bresal saw a huge shapeless mass coming towards them from the east.

'A Fomor!' he shouted, but the Fianna hardly heard him. They looked up half-heartedly from the chess-board and then went back to the game.

As the monster came nearer Mac Bresal saw that it was not one creature but two. The first was the ugliest looking giant that he had ever seen. His enormous body was bloated and swollen; his legs were misshapen and his feet turned inwards. His neck was too long and thin for his body and his head poked forward at a very aggressive angle. He had a thick, unpleasant mouth and long, pointed teeth and that was all that Mac Bresal could see of his face; the rest was covered with bushy hair. Everything about him was dirty; even his weapons were dull and rusty. His shield was old and battered with a rough, blackish surface; neither his sword nor his thick spears looked as if they had been used for years. To complete his battery of arms he dragged a heavy primitive club along the ground after him which tore up the earth like a plough.

The second fomor proved to be a horse. He was even bigger than the giant and twice as ugly, if that was possible. He had thin tangled greyish-black hair which only partly concealed his awkward, bony body. Mac Bresal could count his ribs and the points of his bones. The horse's legs were knotted and twisted and his neck didn't seem to fit on to his shoulders, while his jaws were so long and heavy that they made his head look twice as big as it should. The giant and the horse were engaged in a continuous struggle. The giant was dragging the animal along by a thick halter and the horse was doing its best either to go in the opposite direction or at least to stand still. Every now and then the giant gave him a thump with his iron club and pulled with such force that Mac Bresal thought the horse's head would part company with his body. In return the horse gave such enormous tugs backwards at the halter that it was amazing that the giant's arm wasn't torn out of his shoulder. Mac Bresal had more than the normal amount of courage but when the two hideous creatures came straight towards him he jumped up, sword in hand, and ran as fast as he could to warn the Fianna. This time they listened.

'What is it?' Fionn asked, looking up from the chess-board, but Mac Bresal could only gibber and point across the plain at the approaching monsters. The Fianna jumped up and snatched their arms and stood waiting for the fomors. They didn't seem to be very far away but it took them a long time to reach the hill as they tussled together in their endless tug of war. Finally the giant reached them. He went up to Fionn and bowed his knee and his ugly hairy head and saluted.

'You may rise and speak,' Fionn said, graciously. The Fianna stood by, hands near their weapons and waited.

'Tell us your name and county, I trust it is a noble one?' Fionn asked.

'As to that I cannot say,' the giant replied, 'but I am ready and willing to answer any question you may ask. I am a Fomor of Lochlann, a country to the north of Ireland. I did not know my parents and I have no home but I travel from country to country, serving lords and chiefs. They pay me for my services and in that way I manage to live.'

'I see,' said Fionn, 'and what brings you here?'

'Your fame is known far and wide, Lord Fionn,' the giant said. 'I have heard of your power and your royal bounty and I wish to offer you my services.'

Fionn opened his mouth to speak but the giant ignored him and went on talking.

'I will work for you for a year and at the end of that time I'll fix my own wages. I eat as much at every meal as a hundred men and I am bone idle — that's why I have a horse. I couldn't possibly march with your men. My name is the Gilla Dacker...'

'Gilla Dacker?' asked Fionn, puzzled.

'It means lazy fellow,' the giant told him helpfully.

'Are you?' asked Fionn.

'Very,' replied the giant, 'I am the worst servant in the world and I grumble all the time and, however pleasant and kind my master is, I will always answer with foul words.' The giant's thick lips moved in what presumably passed for a smile. 'Does that answer all your questions?' he asked.

'You don't give much of an account of yourself,' Fionn said, 'but I've never refused any man service or wages yet and I won't turn you away.' Fionn paused, 'A year, you said?'

'A year,' said the Gilla Dacker. He turned to Conán Maol, 'which pays best; the infantry or the horse-service?' he asked.

'O, the horse-service,' Conán Maol answered, 'they get twice as much.'

'Then I will join them,' the giant said, 'since I have a fine steed of my own.' He looked around the company. 'I prefer to tend the horse myself. I don't think anyone here is fit to look after him but I'll let him graze with your animals.'

The Fianna had been listening to the Gilla Dacker with amusement. When, finally, he asked Fionn to place the ugly horse directly under his own royal protection it was too much for them. They burst out laughing and were still doubled up when the Gilla Dacker led his skeletal animal over to the others and took off the halter.

They stopped laughing, however, when the wretched-looking beast, instead of grazing, set about the horses of the Fianna, kicking with his legs, tearing with his teeth and butting with his huge monster head. There was scarcely a horse left in the next few minutes that didn't have a broken leg, or fractured ribs or an ear bitten off, or was in some way mangled for life.

The giant horse then turned his attention to a small field where Conán Maol had his horses but Conán shouted at the Gilla Dacker and told him to take his vicious brute away.

'Or I'll beat the brains out of him myself,' Conán Maol said.

The Gilla Dacker shrugged. 'You'd better get someone to put a halter on him then, but he won't be able to graze and he'll be hungry.'

'Do you think I care?' Conán Maol asked, snatching up the halter. He ran across and jumped the fence and threw the halter around the neck of the huge horse but, pull as he might, he couldn't shift him. The horse-fomor dug his heels into the ground and stiffened his legs and refused to move. Conán Maol was fat and bald and he and the monster made an unlovely sight. The Fianna, who enjoyed seeing Conán Maol discomfitured, waited hopefully for him to make an even bigger fool of himself. Eventually Conán Maol gave up the unequal struggle but kept the halter around the horse's neck and continued to hold on to him. No one made a move to help him and Fergus the Poet went back to the chess-board, still laughing. He waved his hand in the direction of the Gilla Dacker's horse.

'Wouldn't you be better mounting him?' he asked

'Of course, if you are afraid?' Fergus said. The Fianna watched and waited, hiding their smiles behind their hands. There was a titter hurriedly suppressed.

'I'll break your heart, you ugly brute!' Conán Maol shouted at the horse. He jumped up suddenly on to him and began to beat him around the neck with his fists and drove his heels hard into the horse's flanks. The horse stayed as still as a statue and the Fianna were in convulsions again.

'I know what it is,' Fergus said, wiping his eyes. 'He needs the same weight on his back as the Gilla Dacker, and then he'll go.'

'Then come and help me,' Conán Maol shouted.

A couple of the Fianna came over, still grinning, and jumped up behind Conán Maol but the horse still didn't move.

'Come on!' Conán Maol roared.

A few more went over, reluctantly, until finally fifteen of the Fianna were seated very uncomfortably on the bony back of the horse. They beat him with their feet and hands but the horse, stubbornly, stayed quite still. The Gilla Dacker was far from pleased at the way his horse was being treated. He went over to Fionn to complain.

'I can see that all the good things I heard about the Fianna were quite untrue,' he said.

Kylta Mac Ronán drew in his breath. Fionn Mac Cumhal was not accustomed to being addressed in those sort of terms.

'I will not stay with you, not even for a day!' the Gilla Dacker said, loudly. 'You ill-treat my horse, you insult me. Would you or any of your men put up with that? I will not serve you!'

'Just wait a moment. Fionn Mac Cumhal keeps his word. You will stay the year in my service and I will pay you all I promised,' Fionn said.

'Then I will go without wages,' the Gilla Dacker said, 'no man with any honour would stay even one night in camp with such men as yours.' He moved away, turning his back on Fionn, and began to walk away to the south-west. He threw one parting shot over his ungainly shoulder, 'and I will tell the world what I think of Fionn Mac Cumhal and the Fianna,' he said.

The horse raised his ugly head as he saw his master leaving and gave his rattling bones a shake and began to walk slowly and steadily after him. This was too much for the rest of the Fianna: some of them laughed until their ribs were sore; they doubled up and rolled on the ground and held their sides and almost choked.

The Gilla Dacker looked back and saw his horse following him with fifteen of the Fianna still on its back. He paused for a moment to pick up his ragged skirts and then set out with huge giant strides down the hillside. He moved as lightly and as swiftly as a swallow, his feet barely touching the ground. His progress was like the whistle of the wind and the horse pricked up his ears, picked up speed and followed him. The horse's awkward body, however, did not float over the ground as his master's did. His hooves thudded very firmly into every hollow and indentation sending a shudder through his entire frame and the Fianna had a very rough ride indeed. When they saw the distance they had covered in just a few short moments they tried to throw themselves off but they discovered that they were fastened firmly to the horse and all the struggling in the world wasn't going to release them.

'Are you going to let us be carried off by this foul monster?' Conán Maol yelled over his shoulder. His voice was almost lost on the wind but Fionn heard him and seized his sword. The others pulled themselves together and they started off as fast as they could after the Gilla Dacker. The chase led them across Limerick, over the mountains into Kerry, and then up and across the peninsula which thrusts itself far out into the ocean. Only Ligan, one of the fleetest of the Fianna, was able to keep up with them although Fionn never quite lost the Gilla Dacker and the horse from view.

The horse plunged on to the beach at the northern point of the peninsula and Ligan finally overtook him and grabbed his tail. He pulled as hard as he could but the horse went straight on without checking its speed, in through the waves with Conán Maol and the others on his back and Ligan being dragged along behind them. The waters of the sea parted in front of the horse and there was always firm sand under its hooves but the waves closed in immediately again behind them in a raging, swirling torrent. At every moment the men expected to be engulfed but they travelled the whole way across the sea without even a drop of spray touching them.

Fionn stood on the shore with the others until the horse, the Gilla Dacker and the fifteen Fianna were out of sight in the rough waves and then they sank down on to the sand, exhausted after the long chase.

'Has anyone any suggestions?' Fionn asked.

Fergus the Poet stirred, 'I think we should go straight to Ben Edar and get the ship that the Dé Dananns promised us long ago when they were defeated.'

'Do you think they will keep their word?' Fionn asked.

'I have seen such a ship,' Fergus said, 'fitted out and maintained to the last detail.'

On the way to Ben Edar they met two handsome young men wearing scarlet silken cloaks fastened with gold brooches over their armour. They saluted Fionn and told him they had come from the eastern world.

'We want you to judge our skills,' they said.

'My name is Feradach,' said one, 'and I have an axe and a sling-stick and if everyone covers their eyes I can give the sling three blows with the axe.'

'Yes?' said Fionn, puzzled.

'When they uncover their eyes, they will see a ship, ready to sail, inside the harbour.'

Fionn nodded and turned to the other brother.

'My name is Foltebar,' the second young man said, 'and our father is the king of Innia, and I can track the wild duck over nine ridges and nine furrows until I find her nest. I can do the same on the sea, if I have a good boat. We would like to enter your service for a year and then ask you which of us has the better art.'

'We were just talking of such things,' Fionn said. 'Are you of the Dé Dananns?' he asked, suspiciously, but they looked at him blankly.

Fionn didn't have the time to worry about who they might be. 'I will be glad to have you in my service,' he said. 'My own men can track with the best of them but, for the problem that we have now, we need very special skills.' Then he told them about the Gilla Dacker and the way his men had been dragged away through the sea.

'I'll get you a fine ship,' Feradach said, 'and I will be your pilot,' Fotebar added. 'We will find the Gilla Dacker in whichever corner of the earth he might try to hide.'

They set out to the beach and Feradach told them all to cover their heads and they did so. He then struck his sling with his axe and, when they looked up, there was a huge ship complete with oars and sails riding in the harbour.

Then Kylta Mac Ronán went up to the top of the cliff

and gave a great shout which was picked up by the people in the next valley and the next and the next, until all the province of Munster was alerted to the danger. The huntsmen left the chase and marched until a huge body of men finally met together with Fionn at Ben Edar. They held council and it was decided that too many had gone already to risk many more.

'But I must go myself,' Fionn said, and he picked Diarmuid, Goll, Oscar, Fergus the Poet and half a dozen more to go with him and the sons of the king of Innia in pursuit of the Gilla Dacker.

'Who will lead the ones who are left behind?' Goll asked.

'Oisín,' Fionn answered, 'will stay and guard Ireland.'

Fifteen chiefs, led by Fionn, set out in the large, well-equipped ship. They brought gold with them, to use as bribes and a huge quantity of food, because they had no means of knowing how long the voyage would take. The sea was cold and bright. Foltebar took his place at the helm and set a course westward, close on the track of the Gilla Dacker. Soon the shores of Ireland receded out of sight and a storm blew up but Foltebar stayed at his post and never altered course. For three days they ploughed on through mountainous seas with blinding rain and spray until, eventually, the wind died down and the sea grew calm. The darkness lifted and they saw land a little to the west of them. There was a huge rocky cliff so high that the top of it was covered with cloud. Sticking out from the cliff was a round, high rock with slides as slippery as an eel and it was at the foot of this rock that the trail of the Gilla Dacker came to an end.

Foltebar jumped ashore and examined the cliff carefully.

'He must live at the top of that,' he said.

'But there is no way up it!' said Diarmuid.

'I understood,' said Fergus the Poet, chosing his words so that each one was as sharp as the point of an axe, 'I understood that you studied the druid arts with the Dé Dananns and that you were skilled above all others in champion feats.'

'That is so,' Diarmuid replied.

'Then all that learning must have been wasted if, when we most need them, your talents can't find us a way up that rock.'

Diarmuid flushed with annoyance and he reached for the druid staves Manannán had given him years before. He glared at Fergus then drove one of the staves into the ground and took a giant leap and landed on top of the jutting rock. He looked down at the Fianna; his face twisted with his famous battle anger. He raised his spear and gave a great cry then turned and began to climb ledge by ledge up the face of the cliff. The sun glinted on his helmet and the men below shaded their eyes and watched him anxiously.

When he got to the top he stopped for a moment and looked over the other side of the cliff. He saw a beautiful flowery plain in front of him. He could hear birds singing and the soft humming of bees; there was a rustle of a gentle breeze through little groups of graceful trees and, in the distance, the tinkling and gurgling of a stream and waterfall. Diarmuid caught his breath with the peace and beauty of it all. He looked back once at Fionn and then, realising that there was no way to get his companions up the cliff after him, he decided to explore the plain.

He had not gone far when he came to a great tree laden with fruit, beside a group of pillar-stones and a bubbling well of clear water. He was thirsty and he bent to drink but, before his lips could touch the water he heard the heavy tread of a group of soldiers and he jumped up, his hand on his sword. The noise stopped immediately and when he looked around there was no one there. He bent to the pool again and the same thing happened: there was a clamour of marching and armour but when he looked up, still thirsty, the plain was empty. His eye was then caught by a beautiful enamelled drinking horn, chased with gold, lying on one of the pillar-stones. I should have used this, he thought. He picked it up, filled it then drank deeply until his thirst was slaked. He sighed with satisfaction then wiped his mouth and had another look around him. Coming towards him was a Man of Enchantment, a wizard-champion with long, flowing yellow hair held by a circle of gold. He was fully armed with a shield, sword and spear and his coat of mail was partly covered by a silken cloak. His manner, however, was neither golden nor silky.

'Isn't this plain big enough, Diarmuid of Erin, and isn't there water enough in its crystal springs but still you have to steal my drinking horn and come to my island without my leave or permission?'

He leaped upon Diarmuid and they began to fight, fist to fist and sword to sword and knee to knee. The wizard-champion had magic powers but they were not enough to shield him from the strength of a warrior like Diarmuid. They were matched like two mighty lions or two strong serpents and, at the end of the day, when neither had gained an advantage, the wizard jumped out of range of Diarmuid's sword and jumped into the well.

Diarmuid stood at the edge of the wall and peered down into it. There was no sign of the wizard; there wasn't even a bubble of water to show where he had gone. Diarmuid didn't want to go back to the Fianna with such an inconclusive story so he decided to stay on. He hunted and killed a deer and cut strips from the flesh, cooked them and washed down the meal with more water from the well and finally slept. In the morning the wizard was waiting for him by the pillar-stone.

'Isn't it enough that you drink my water, without trespassing in my woods, killing my deer?' the wizard shouted and leaped upon Diarmuid again. They fought as before, well matched, neither gaining on the other but, this time, when the Man of Enchantment slid out of reach and was about to jump into the well, Diarmuid caught hold of his arm and, as a result, found himself at the bottom of the well with him. All he could see was darkness and dim shadows. They seemed to have fallen for miles, deeper and deeper, but Diarmuid wasn't hurt. Suddenly they were in bright sunshine. The wizard wrested himself from Diarmuid's grip and ran off into a lovely valley filled with every kind of flower. The surrounding hills were covered with red yew trees and, not far off, lay a city of tall houses. One house had the proportions of a palace and on the lawn a group of knights were amusing themselves with sword play and jousting. The wizard was going in this direction but too quickly for Diarmuid to catch him. The palace gates opened for the Enchanted Man and then the knights closed in behind him and turned to face Diarmuid with threatening shouts.

Diarmuid's battle anger took over and he lay about the knights and rushed through their ranks like a hawk among a flock of sparrows and they scattered up into the hills and woods to hide. Then, exhausted, Diarmuid sat down on the now empty lawns. He was covered with scratches and small wounds and he felt that he would never see his friends again. He lay down and closed his eyes and finally, utterly weary, he fell into a deep sleep.

He was woken abruptly by a blow with the flat side of a sword and he started up to find a tall, handsome young man of commanding appearance standing over him. He went for his own sword but the stranger spoke to him quickly in a friendly voice.

'I am not an enemy. I came to warn you that this is a dangerous place and to ask you to come with me where you will be welcome and cared for.'

'Very well,' Diarmuid said. He was confused from all that had happened to him and it was a few moments before he remembered to thank the young man. They walked for a long time until they came to another city where Diarmuid was brought to a house. He was given fresh clothes and attendants prepared a bath for him and then his wounds were treated with herbs. Afterwards there was a great feast in an enormous banqueting hall. Diarmuid was amazed at the luxury of the meal and the elegance of the guests. There were over a hundred fine young warriors and almost as many modest blushing young women. They all had long shining hair falling on their shoulders like a mantle of gold. One in particular was extremely beautiful. Her dress was sewn with gold thread and she wore the flowing veil of a queen. There was wine and music and feasting long into the night and, when it was over, Diarmuid was given gifts of gold and silver and jewels. Finally he was brought to an ornate bed and fell asleep on thick soft down, still not knowing where he was or who his hosts were.

In the morning he went to find the young prince who had brought him there.

'You have shown me such kindness,' Diarmuid said, 'and I would like to know the name of this country and how to thank you.'

'This is the Land-Under-Wave,' the prince said, 'and I am only repaying kindness shown to me in the past by Fionn Mac Cumal. I spent a year at his court, although I don't think you remember me.'

Diarmuid shook his head and then the prince went on, 'the man who fought you at the well is the king of this land and he has taken part of my patrimony.' He lifted his hands expressively. 'We live here in exile. My warriors are trained and ready but...' he hesitated, then smiled, 'I think Diarmuid of the Love Spot came to us when he was needed.'

'If I can help?' Diarmuid said.

'Fight with us against the Knight of the Fountain and you will be welcome in my house forever,' the prince said, and they shook hands on it and pledged themselves to eternal friendship.

In the meantime Fionn had a similar kind of experience. At first he waited with his followers at the foot of the cliff but when after a few days there was no sign either of the Gilla Dacker and his horse or Conán Maol, Fionn became very worried. Foltebar offered to go on in search of

Diarmuid but Fionn decided that they should all go together. They took some cables from the ship and made firm ropes with them and slowly, one by one, they reached the top of the cliff.

They found Diarmuid's tracks and the remains of his meals and then the traces of the battle on the lawn in front of the palace. As they stood there, wondering what had happened, a young nobleman came riding across the plain towards them. He had the air of a royal and his beautiful chestnut horse had a bridle of gold and a splendid jewelled saddle. The young man jumped from his horse and embraced Fionn.

'You are welcome to my country,' he said. 'I am the king of Sorcha and you are my most welcome guests.'

They were brought to a huge palace with tall towers and a carved front and they were immediately given comfortable rooms while baths were being prepared. The people were gentle and made them welcome and there was food and sparkling wine and strong ales in such quantity that they all became light-headed.

'I have never seen a feast so well ordered,' Fionn said.

'Nor have we ever had the pleasure of so distinguished a guest as Fionn Mac Cumhal,' the king replied, politely. 'But I do not understand why you are such a small party,' he went on. 'Where are the rest of your followers?'

So Fionn told him the whole story, about the Gilla Dacker and his horse and the way his men had been kidnapped. 'We have come to look for Conán Maol and the fifteen Fianna who are with him, and we must also search for Diarmuid who is now missing too,' Fionn said.

'You may take as many of my men to help you as you wish,' said the king of Sorcha, but just then a messenger rushed in. He was covered with dust and grime and out of breath. He bowed low to the king and then gasped out his message.

'There is a foreign fleet at our shores and the enemy has already started to plunder and burn our country. They say it is the king of Greece. He has conquered every country he has invaded and he wants to rule the whole world.'

The king of Sorcha turned to Fionn with a look of great distress and Fionn knew what was wanted of him. 'We will leave the search for the Gilla Dacker for the time being,' he said, 'and go together to defend your country from the Greeks. It will not be the first time we've met them on the battlefield,' he said, 'and they've never beaten us yet.'

The war with the king of Greece went exactly as Fionn expected. The combined strength of the king of Sorcha's armies and the Fianna made piecemeal out of the foreign champions. Each day a fresh wave of invaders came ashore from the fleet and each day they were driven back having lost their best men. After several such days the king of Greece called a meeting of his chiefs.

'It's the Sons of the Gael,' he said, in disgust. 'We would have beaten the king of Sorcha by now but for Fionn Mac Cumhal.'

'We've had bad luck since we landed here,' one of the chiefs said, 'I suggest we leave now with what few men we have left. There's no hope of conquering Sorcha while the Fianna are here.'

The next day, when the people of Sorcha and the Fianna went down to the shore they found nothing left in the harbour except a few broken pieces of timber floating in the water and some hurriedly dug graves along the shore-line. They were in the middle of congratulating each other on their success when they saw a troop of soldiers carrying banners and standards riding towards them.

'Fergus, go and see who they are,' Fionn ordered and Fergus set out across the plain. He hadn't gone far when he recognised Diarmuid at the head of the troop and he ran to embrace him.

It took hours for them all to tell their separate adventures. Diarmuid had helped the young prince to defeat the king of Land-Under-Wave and the prince was now king with all his rightful lands restored to him

'We have sent the king of Greece packing,' Fionn said with satisfaction, 'and now we can all go in search of the Gilla Dacker.'

'My people have druidical arts,' said the king of Land-Under-Wave, 'and we've discovered that the Gilla Dacker is Avarta the Dé Danann and he has the fifteen Fianna imprisoned in the Land of Promise. I suggest we start the search again from the rocky cliff where the tracks stopped.'

Fionn agreed and both the king of Sorcha and the king of Land-Under-Wave gave some of their best men to help him. This time Foltebar found the track at once. It went across the plain to the sea and so they brought their ship around and then sailed from island to island and, even though the Gilla Dacker had tried everything to cover his tracks, they came eventually to the Land of Promise. Diarmuid recognised it at once: as a boy he had been nurtured there and instructed in the druid arts by the Sea King, Manannán Mac Lir.

'We'll burn and pillage every inch of it,' Fionn said, jumping from the ship but Diarmuid held him back.

'These people can cast every manner of spell. It would be better to send a message to Avarta to ask him to set our men free. If he refused then we can make war.'

'There has been enough delay,' Fionn said, but Foltebar offered to find the track and to take one single companion and be back in the shortest possible time. Reluctantly Fionn agreed.

Foltebar had no trouble in finding Avarta's palace, even though the way was crooked and full of shadowy valleys and confusing forks in the road. They found Conán Maol and his companions on the lawn in front of the palace, captive, but fairly free to roam within the palace confines. Then Avarta came out himself and greeted Foltebar.

'What brings you here?' he asked.

'Fionn is waiting a little distance away with a great army. He has sent us to demand your prisoners; otherwise he will attack.'

'I see,' said Avarta. He rubbed his face thoughtfully. He had been sure that he had covered his tracks successfully and if Fionn had got so far, and with an army too, it might be wiser to send back a peaceful answer.

'I will come with you,' he said, eventually, 'and speak to Fionn Mac Cumhal myself.'

He consulted briefly with his council and found that they had separately arrived at the same conclusion. So, by the end of the day, Fionn and his men were made welcome in Avarta's palace and a great feast was prepared. The celebrations went on for three days and nights and, on the fourth day, Fionn was asked what compensation he wanted for the inconveniences done to him.

'I will not ask for anything,' Fionn said, grandly. He had been well fed and perhaps too well wined. 'In fact I will pay you the wages you asked me when you came to my service.'

'Just a minute,' Conán Maol said, 'you haven't suffered what I've suffered. You didn't ride for days and nights on that bag of bones that passes for a horse. You didn't push your way through rough undergrowth and have your legs torn to bits and you didn't cross the sea through mountainous waves and think that every moment was your last. Because if you had, you would ask for a fine reward.'

It was Avarta's turn to laugh at Conán Maol, 'name your reward,' he said, trying to keep his face straight, 'because I've heard of your foul tongue and I've no wish to have it used on me.'

'All right,' Conán Maol said. He thought for a moment. 'Choose fifteen of your best men, your dearest friends in fact, and make them get up on that brute of a horse. You can hold on to the tail and go back to Erin the way you brought me and my companions.'

This effectively stopped Avarta and his companions laughing but a promise was a promise and Avarta agreed.

'At least Conán Maol didn't ask for gold and treasure,' Fionn whispered to Goll. 'We would never hear the end of that; the Fianna would be disgraced forever.'

They made their ship ready and took a pleasant enough leave of Avarta and then they set sail back to Ireland. Avarta chose his men and caught the tail of the lumbering horse and they followed Fionn by exactly the same track as before, all the way back to Munster. The Fianna had made camp again and they saw the Gilla Dacker, as before, when he was a long way off. He had let go of the tail and was running before the horse and his fifteen warriors were being jolted uncomfortably on top of it.

'You made a good choice,' Fionn said, grinning, to Conán Maol.

The Gilla Dacker came up to them. He had a far from pleasant expression on his face.

'It's a fine sight,' Fionn said.

'Then make the most of it,' the Gilla Dacker said. He was angry and out of breath. 'You'll never get the chance to laugh at me again!'

His men began to dismount and then the giant stepped forward suddenly and pointed over the heads of the Fianna to where their horses were standing.

The Fianna, remembering what he had done before, moved as one man to protect their animals but they could see nothing except a field of peacefully grazing horses. Fionn turned back to invite the Gilla Dacker to his tent to smooth things over but the horse, the giant and the fifteen warriors of Avarta had disappeared as if they had never existed and neither Fionn nor any of his men ever saw them again.

HOW DIARMUID GOT HIS LOVE SPOT

One day when Diarmuid, Conall, Goll and Oscar were out hunting they stayed too late and could not get back before nightfall. They spent the early part of the evening picking berries in the woods and eating them but they soon got tired of that and, when about midnight, they saw a light in the distance Conall hurried the others towards it.

'Surely they will give us shelter,' he said.

An old man welcomed them at the door of the cottage.

'Is it the Fianna?' he asked, peering at them through the shadows.

Goll stepped into the pool of light by the door. 'Four of the Fianna,' he said. 'We are very hungry and would be glad of anything you can give us.'

'Daughter!' the old man shouted, and a young girl came out from the back of the house. 'Conall, Goll, Oscar and Diarmuid are here. Make some food for them.'

'How did he know our names?' Oscar asked, in a low voice and Goll shushed him as the old man invited them in and brought them over to the fire.

'There is only myself, the girl and the cat,' he said, pushing the cat away from the hearth, 'but you are welcome to share what we have.'

It didn't take the girl long to prepare a meal and soon the six of them were sitting around the table eating. A few moments later there was a sudden noise from the back of the house and a ram leaped into the room, and up on to the table.

'Go and tie it up, Conall,' Goll said.

'Why should I do it?' Conall said.

'Because it'll eat your dinner if you don't,' Goll said, and went on eating.

Conall gave Goll an angry look and then got up and pulled at the rope round the ram's neck. He tried to drag it towards the back of the house but the ram gave a great shake and threw Conall to the floor and put one hoof on top of him to hold him down.

'You'd better deal with it, Diarmuid,' Goll said, laughing.

So Diarmuid got up and went to try to pull the ram off Conall who was complaining bitterly. The ram shook himself again and, with a twist of his body, put Diarmuid on the floor under another hoof.

Goll and Oscar looked at each other. They were afraid to look at the old man and the girl. Oscar realised from Goll's expression that the honour of the Fianna was at stake so he got up and pulled at the ram with all his strength. But the ram, who had obviously perfected his shaking trick, succeeded in putting Oscar under a third hoof.

Goll leaped up encouraged by shouts from his trapped companions and tugged with all his might at the ram but ended up the same way as the others. The ram now had one of the Fianna under each hoof and there was nothing they could do about it.

'It was your idea, of course,' Goll said to Conall, 'to come here for your dinner.'

'That's an awful thing,' the old man said to the ram, 'to do to the brave Fianna of Ireland.' He turned to the cat, 'you'd better take the ram back to where he was tied up,' he said.

The cat got up, stretched himself, then went over to the ram, picked up the rope in its mouth and led the ram, unprotestingly, to the back of the house and tied him up. The four on the floor rubbed their bruises and got up feeling extremely foolish.

'Come back and finish the food,' the old man said, and they brushed themselves down and went back to the table, but their appetite had gone.

'We can't,' Goll said, 'we have been humiliated.'

'Eat,' said the old man, 'and afterwards I will show you that you are braver than anyone else.'

Reluctantly they began to pick at the food and managed to eat a little more, but without much enthusiasm. Afterwards, as the girl was clearing the table, the old man beckoned them over to the fire again. He pointed to Goll. 'You are the bravest man in the world because you have wrestled with the world.'

'I don't understand,' Goll said.

'That ram is the world,' the old man said.

Oscar looked at Conall, 'what sort of a place have you brought us to?' he said, under his breath. 'Either the old man is mad or the place is enchanted.'

'The ram is the world?' Goll asked.

'Yes,' the old man said, 'but death will come to the world.'

'I suppose it will,' Goll said.

'That is death,' the old man continued, pointing to the cat.

The four Fianna glanced at each other uneasily but, after a while, the talk became general. They discussed the hunt and the rising salmon and the old man told them the direction to take back to the Hill of Allen on the following day and there was no more talk of death and the world.

The girl came back into the room and the old man said that their beds were ready.

'Go into the inner room,' he said, pointing to the door, 'you may sleep there.'

They found several beds in the room and soon made themselves comfortable.

'This is a strange house,' Goll whispered, as he got under the covers.

'But at least we are warm,' Conall said.

A few moments later the girl came to sleep in the room with them and her beauty lit the room with a golden light.

Conall couldn't resist her. He got up and went over to

her bed and made to get in with her.

'Go back to your bed, Conall,' she said. It was the first time she had spoken. 'I belonged to you once, but long ago.'

'I don't remember,' Conall said, 'who are you?'

She didn't answer for a moment, and then she said, 'I will never belong to you again,' and so Conall went sadly back to his bed.

Oscar pushed back his covers.

'Where are you going, Oscar?' the girl asked.

'Over to you,' he answered, suiting the action to the words.

'No,' she said. 'I belonged to you once, too, but never again,' and Oscar hesitated for a moment and then went back to his bed.

Then Diarmuid got up and went over to her.

'What do you want, Diarmuid?' she asked.

'You,' he said, bending over her.

'I belonged to you once,' she said. 'Don't you know me?'

He tried, gallantly, for a few moments to remember, then shook his head. 'No,' he replied, 'but I would like to know you now.'

'I can never belong to you again. My name is Youth ' she said. Four long deep sighs filled the room and Goll, who had been about to try his luck, pulled the covers back over his head and turned to the wall. The girl put her arms up to Diarmuid.

'But stay here a moment, Diarmuid,' she said, 'and I will put a mark on you so that every woman who sees you will love you.' So she put her hand to his forehead and left a spot there and no woman ever afterwards refused Diarmuid her love.

THE ABDUCTION OF EARGNA

The Fianna were strong and brave and — usually — honourable; they never chose a wife for her money, nor offered a woman violence; they gave whatever was asked of them and they never ran away from a challenge.

Unfortunately they were also human and Fionn, their leader, was even more human. He had been chosen not because he was bigger or stronger or braver than any one of them but because his father and grandfather before him had held the position. He stayed in power because in addition to his warrior skills he had subtlety and cunning.

The Fianna, then, were his men and it was inevitable that from time to time they used their power to settle a few personal scores. It was in the course of just such a personal vendetta that Fionn killed his uncle, Ronan, and with him the Grey Man of Luachair.

Ronan's son, Aodh Rinn, and the Grey Man's son, Conán, demanded compensation. Both men were liked and respected as brave warriors throughout Ireland and Scotland and Fionn decided that it would be much more prudent to make peace with them rather than have them fight against him. So he agreed to their demands with uncharacteristic docility and invited them to join the Fianna.

For a while all appeared well on the surface. The Fianna continued their summer hunting and their winter duties but Aodh was not entirely satisfied with the compensation he had got and he still resented the way his father had been killed.

He decided to leave the Fianna to their huge feasts or venison, salmon and game. He could not bear to sit with

them at night, beside their immense fires, watching them
drink and listening to them boasting.

'I'm going back to my own fort,' he told Fionn one day,
'you have plenty of warriors.'

'None as brave as you,' Fionn said, looking at him warily.

Aodh shrugged, 'the whole world knows we have made
peace. We do not have to spend the rest of our lives
together.'

'As you wish,' Fionn said, 'if you do not like the life —'

'It is not only that. I would like to be with my daughter.'

'Eargna?' Fionn smiled, 'they say she is the loveliest girl
in Ireland.'

'That is as may be,' Aodh said, 'I only know that I miss
her very much and that she is growing and needs protection.'

'You will soon have young warriors coming to court her,'
Conán Maol remarked. Fionn gave him a look. It was common knowledge that Aodh would give short shrift to any
young man who dared brave his stronghold.

'There will be no warriors,' Aodh said, 'and no courting.'
He raised his voice so that they could all hear him. 'Any
man who tries it will feel the sharp edge of my sword.'

'He is a man of his word,' Conán Maol said, behind his
hand.

'Oscar is looking for you, Conán Maol,' Fionn said
sharply and for once his henchman, who was not called
Conán of the Foul Tongue for nothing, took the hint and
left the subject of Eargna alone.

But it had given Fionn something to think about. He was
uneasy having Aodh and Conán of Luachair in the Fianna
but at least he could keep an eye on them. If Aodh retired
to his distant estate he could brood and plot and nibble
away at Fionn's authority and no one would be the wiser
until it was too late. Nevertheless he bid Aodh an affection-
ate farewell and told him he would always be welcome in
the Fianna camp. 'And you will always find a welcome in
my house,' Aodh said, in return. Their eyes met briefly,

then Aodh called his servants and jumped into his chariot. Fionn watched until the party was out of sight.

'It is good to be welcome in his house,' he said to Conán Maol, 'and as you say Aodh never breaks his word.'

'He won't break it over his daughter, either,' Conán Maol said, sharp as ever.

'I hadn't forgotten,' Fionn replied.

The truce lasted exactly four years and seven months. During that time Aodh had lived quietly and peacefully with Eargna. No warriors had been brave enough to try for her hand, despite her beauty and good nature, although many had been very tempted. Conán, the son of the Grey Man of Luachair, had remained peaceably with the Fianna but Fionn was by no means certain that all the old wounds had healed.

Then Conán's wife died. Her name was Liffe and she was noble and beautiful and the great river which springs between the two mountains still bears her name. Conán of Luachair was beside himself with grief. He brooded alone and no one could rouse him out of his apathy.

'So now I have two erstwhile enemies,' Fionn thought, 'one locked up with his daughter in a remote castle and possibly plotting mischief; the other, bereaved, upsetting my camp with his long face and probably brooding over past injuries.' It occurred to him that if they should get together over a certain purpose he might dispose of them both, or rather they would dispose of each other.

He went to Conán of Luachair's tent.

'You have lost the fairest of the fair,' Fionn said to Conán.

'She was the best above all others.'

'There is only one other in all of Ireland to come near her,' Fionn said.

'No,' Conán said, shaking his head. 'There is no one.'

'Have you forgotten the daughter of Aodh?' Fionn asked.

A brief flicker of interest passed across Conán's face and

then he lapsed into gloom again. 'I have heard that she is lovely,' he said, 'but Aodh has sworn that no man will have her.'

'Are you, Conán of Luachair, going to ignore a challenge like that?'

'It is not a challenge to me,' Conán pointed out.

'A warrior who has won so many victories?' Fionn went on, as if Conán hadn't spoken.

'If I was to take another wife,' Conán said slowly, 'if I did, then perhaps Eargna would be the one.'

'It is a pity then,' Fionn said, 'that Aodh has her locked away so securely in his castle.'

Then having dropped the seed on what seemed to be promisingly fertile ground he bid Conán good-day and left him to his thoughts.

A few weeks later Conán of Luachair suddenly stopped brooding and came to Fionn with a request.

'Will you give me some men to cross the Suir and support me in a possible attack?'

'To what purpose?' Fionn asked, blandly.

'I am going to demand Eargna's hand from Aodh.'

'There are twelve times twenty trained warriors waiting for just such an adventure,' Fionn said, 'and you may take them with a heart and a half.'

The band set out a few days later and Fionn smiled as he watched them go. Plans, however, seldom go exactly as one wishes.

Aodh was missing from his stronghold when Conán arrived with the fierce Fianna soldiers. He had gone on a raid to Breifne and his servants admitted the visitors as friends.

Eargna recognised Conán and made him welcome. She had been locked up in the fortress for a long time and, much as she loved her father, she would also have liked the companionship of men of her own age. It wasn't very difficult for Conán to persuade her to be his wife. Eargna was in the frame of mind to accept anyone who was person-

112

able and well-born.

'In any case,' said Oisín, Fionn's son, who was holding a watching brief for his father, 'you can carry her off by force if necessary.'

It wasn't necessary. Eargna made her preparations quickly and ordered one of her women to accompany them. The group left as peaceably as they had come and were over the Suir and into Leinster before Aodh returned.

At first Aodh was furious. He had had a difficult few weeks with his men; the raid on Breifne had not been very successful and he had been looking forward to Eargna's company on his return.

'Where is she?' he demanded, grabbing his chief steward by the throat.

'They came with swords and spears and...' The steward choked then rushed into a torrent of excuses when Aodh released him.

'Who did?' Aodh demanded.

'Hundreds of the Fianna,' the steward said.

'Fionn Mac Cumhal?' Aodh asked.

'No, he wasn't with them. I could not stop them, lord, we were hopelessly outnumbered.'

'Who?' Aodh asked again, 'who led them? I will kill him.'

'It was Conán, son of the Grey Man of Luachair,' the steward said and suddenly Aodh's anger was gone.

'My friend,' he said slowly, 'my poor friend who loves me.' He went to the casement and looked out over the lawns. 'He is a hero worthy of her,' he said to himself and tried not to think how lonely the castle would be without Eargna. 'I can't fight Conán of Luachair.' He turned back to the steward. 'You did well not to resist them. I wish them joy.' The steward rubbed his throat and hurried away thankful that his head was still on his shoulders.

It was Fionn's turn to brood. The two houses of Aodh and Conán were now united by a happy and successful marriage. He could only wait for an opportunity to taunt Aodh with breaking his vow to kill any aspiring son-in-law.

The opportunity wasn't too long in coming. The Irish lords met some months later at the Boyne and, as always at great feasts, the usual amount of boasting went on.

'I', Oscar said, spitting out salmon bones, 'would never retreat from an enemy no matter who he was, or however easy it might be. I would stand firm, nay, I would pursue him for the rest of his life.'

Aodh was listening, 'if you can fulfil that vow, you will indeed live the sweet life,' he commented. 'I too have always met my foes face to face and never broken my word.'

'Except to let your daughter be kidnapped,' Fionn said, in a clear voice.

'Not so!' Aodh shouted, 'she is wed to my dear friend.'

'Without wedding gifts, without supervised courtship?' Fionn asked. 'The way I heard it Conán of Luachair came to your castle with armed men and took her against her will.'

'If that is what men say,' Aodh shouted, his temper rising, 'then I will not be dishonoured. I will take my daughter home across the Suir.'

'Words are easy,' Fionn said. He picked up a haunch of pork. 'Will you taste the champion's portion?' he asked, silkily.

Aodh didn't reply. He stood up, buckling on his sword.

'I would suggest,' Fionn said, in the same smooth voice, 'that you ask the son of the Grey Man for compensation.'

He listened, smiling, to the shouts and hoof beats of Aodh's men as their lord rallied them to set out immediately on a raiding party.

'That is what you wanted?' Conán Maol said, 'isn't it?' As usual he had been listening, 'a feud?'

'More than a feud,' Fionn said, 'a duel.'

'They are old friends. There will be hard words passed but they won't kill each other,' Oscar said.

'If you think that,' Fionn replied, with a note of triumph, 'then you haven't heard about Oisín.'

An appreciative smile crossed Conán Maol's face, 'I hadn't thought of that.'

At first Aodh had some trouble in finding Conán and Eargna. He went to Leinster to Conán's stronghold and there he was told what it appeared every man, woman and household dog in Ireland knew, except himself, that Oisín had fallen in love with Eargna. It had happened when he first set eyes on her when he went with Conán of Luachair to raid Aodh's castle.

For a while he had succeeded in controlling his feelings. He rode beside Eargna as she went with Conán to be his bride and he watched the apparent happiness of the newly married couple for a few months. Then he could stand it no longer. He made love to her in spite of her protests — he was not the son of Fionn Mac Cumhal for nothing — and Conán, furious, went into the mountains where he made no raids, took no rents and spoke to no one but his steward for the best part of a year.

Aodh found Conán eventually at the foot of the Erne.

'You think you can hide from me,' Aodh demanded, brandishing his sword. It gleamed bright silver in the spray from the waterfall.

'Not from you,' Conán said.

'I want my bride price,' Aodh said, 'you took my daughter! You cannot escape giving me my due.'

Conán laughed without humour.

'You may have her back then,' he said, 'otherwise — nothing.'

'You have dishonoured me,' Aodh shouted.

'We are all dishonoured,' Conán said. He drew his sword and faced Aodh.

Conán's steward tried to intervene. 'Surely,' he said, 'your quarrel is with Oisín, both of you?'

Conán smiled sarcastically. 'The daughter of Aodh certainly prefers him, or if not him, who now? You kept her locked up too long, old friend.'

'You insult me and now you have insulted my daughter,'

115

Aodh roared. 'I demand satisfaction.'

'Then you shall have it!' Conán said. 'Fetch my shield!'

They went to the Island of Birds for the duel. Some of the Fianna were sent by Fionn to watch and to report to him. Many of them disapproved of the way it had been brought about and they went reluctantly.

Aodh and Conán of Luachair were both warrior-champions and they gave each other blow for blow in a long, exhausting battle until, finally, Aodh slipped through Conán's defences and cut his head to the bone. Conán faced his former father-in-law with bared teeth. Blood streamed from his wound and his mouth was twisted with anger. He was not a pleasant sight. He lurched forward, then hesitated and measured his distance, drew back his arm and swept off Aodh's head with one hero-blow.

Aodh was buried there on the island and Conán was carried back to his Leinster home by his attendants. A subdued party of men went back to report to Fionn. It had not been a happy day for Ireland. Conán of Luachair lay in bed for five long weeks. The wound should have healed in a few days but it was as if all the evil and venom of the quarrel had entered his blood. He made a partial recovery but only survived Aodh by a year. He died after a brainstorm lasting two days and they said that a poisoned worm had entered his head when Aodh struck him.

The episode did not cure Oisín of romantic dalliance. We do not know what happened to Eargna but we do know that for many years Fionn continued as before, his fighting force tightened and strengthened by the treacherous weeding out of two courageous warriors.

But even Fionn Mac Cumhal could not live forever, although some say he still roams remote mountains and glens in another form. He fell, it is believed, by the sword but others have it that it was by the hand of a fisherman. Afterwards the power of the Fianna was broken forever by Cairbre, the High King.

Oisín made a fair attempt at immortality. He went to

Tír-na-n-óg with the lovely Niamh and survived the Fianna for hundreds of years. It was only when he came back and was turned into a trembling old man that he finally gave up women.

In his last remaining years he spent a lot of time talking about the old days with Saint Patrick.

'Fionn should not have brought about those heroes' deaths,' he said, staring at the saint with his sightless eyes. 'They are all gone now, the brave Fianna, Oscar, Goll, Conán Maol and all my friends. Ireland is full of grey-faced foreigners.'

'Who would look at me now, old and despicable?' he asked. 'Not Niamh, not Eargna and all the lovely gentle women. They are all gone too. Once,' he said, with the beginning of a shadowy smile,'once I had yellow hair and women loved me.'

FABLES AND LEGENDS OF IRELAND
Maureen Donegan

These fascinating tales were told and retold by word of mouth down through the years. Although they are full of magical creatures and enchanted castles they are also about people: real people who suffered from indigestion and jealousy, just like us. Ailill and Maeve compare their possessions; the discussion quickly becomes an argument because Ailill has his own bull, the Finnbennach and Maeve must have a better one. She assembles all the warriors of her kingdom to fight for the possession of the magical bull, the Donn Cuailnge.

Maildun travels the seven seas, battling with bizarre and fantastic monsters, to search for the man who killed his father. He falls by the wayside more than once, particularly when there is a beautiful woman involved, but eventually arrives home to a hero's welcome.

Fionn Mac Cumhal and his band of followers spend their days hunting, fishing and protecting damsels in distress. They have a little trouble with their wives, who do not always care to be left by the fireside but when they have an evening out together in a local tavern it leads to disaster. Oisín is spirited away to Tír-na-n-Óg by the lovely Niamh but, before he dies, he has the satisfaction of getting the better of St. Patrick. The Fianna, though larger than life and swashbuckling across Ireland even into fairy cities, live on, in spirit if not in flesh, in an Ireland which is much changed since giants and heroes strode across it.

THE FIRST BOOK OF IRISH MYTHS AND LEGENDS
Eoin Neeson

Eoin Neeson delves deep into the past and comes up with plenty of intrigue, romance and excitement in these stories about our Firbolg and Milesian forbears. He retells his stories with a directness and simplicity which makes them refreshingly modern. *The First Book of Irish Myths and Legends* contains 'The Tale of the Children of Tuireann', 'The Wooing of Etain', 'The Combat at the Ford' and 'Deirdre and the Sons of Usna'.

THE SECOND BOOK OF IRISH MYTHS AND LEGENDS
Eoin Neeson

Again more fascinating legends from Eoin Neeson. Included are 'The Children of Lir', the classic story of 'Diarmuid and Grainne' and an unusual story about Cuchulainn.

ENCHANTED IRISH TALES
Patricia Lynch

Enchanted Irish Tales tells of ancient heroes and heroines, fantastic deeds of bravery, magical kingdoms, weird and wonderful animals ... This new illustrated edition of classical folktales, retold by Patricia Lynch with all the imagination and warmth for which she is renowned, rekindles the age-old legends of Ireland, as exciting today as they were when first told. This collection includes:

Conary Mór and the Three Red Riders
The Long Life of Tuan Mac Carrell
Finn Mac Cool and the Fianna
Oisin and the Land of Youth
The Kingdom of the Dwarfs
The Dragon Ring of Connla
Mac Datho's Boar
Ethne

THE CHILDREN'S BOOK OF
IRISH FOLKTALES
Kevin Danaher

These tales are filled with the mystery and adventure of a land of lonely country roads and isolated farms, humble cottages and lordly castles, rolling fields and tractless bogs. They tell of giants and ghosts, of queer happenings and wondrous deeds, of fairies and witches and of fools and kings.